GUIDE FOR SAFETY
IN THE
CHEMICAL LABORATORY

PREPARED BY AND PUBLISHED FOR

THE GENERAL SAFETY COMMITTEE
OF THE
MANUFACTURING CHEMISTS'
ASSOCIATION, INC.
Washington, D.C.

FOURTH PRINTING

D. VAN NOSTRAND COMPANY, INC.
PRINCETON, NEW JERSEY

TORONTO   LONDON

NEW YORK

D. VAN NOSTRAND COMPANY, INC.
120 Alexander St., Princeton, New Jersey (*Principal office*)
24 West 40 Street, New York 18, New York

D. VAN NOSTRAND COMPANY, LTD.
358, Kensington High Street, London, W.14, England

D. VAN NOSTRAND COMPANY (Canada), LTD.
25 Hollinger Road, Toronto 16, Canada

Library of Congress Catalog Card No.: 54-7536

First Printing, June, 1954
Second Printing, August, 1954
Third Printing, September, 1962
Fourth Printing, August, 1966

PRINTED IN THE UNITED STATES OF AMERICA

Dedicated to the memory of Mr. D. O. Mason, the first Chairman of the Manufacturing Chemists' Association's General Safety Committee, for his untiring efforts and contributions to safety in the Chemical Industry.

THE GENERAL SAFETY COMMITTEE

Foreword

The Manufacturing Chemists' Association subscribes to the maxim that

"Chemicals in any form can be safely stored, handled, and used if their hazardous physical and chemical properties are fully understood and the necessary precautions, including the use of proper safeguards and personal protective equipment, are observed."

To implement this principle, the management of every unit within a manufacturing establishment must give wholehearted support to a well integrated safety policy. The importance of management interest cannot be overemphasized, because employees take their cue from "the boss" on matters of safety as on other plant business.

Once management accepts this responsibility, its principal problem is to determine the best method of disseminating safety information throughout its organization. One of the constructive measures by which the Association has advanced uniform safety standards is the publication of Chemical Safety Data Sheets. There is little doubt that this effort contributed to the knowledge and understanding of the hazards of chemicals and improvement of their safe handling throughout the industry. One of the principal contributions to general safety is the coordinated effort by all technical committees.

Since the industry produces and distributes a large variety of chemicals—many of them new—each year, the number of related hazards increases very rapidly from year to year. As a consequence, training in safety consciousness is of growing importance, not only within the industry itself, but in the schools that supply new personnel. Although on-the-job training, particularly during recent years, has been a substantial aid in improving the attitude of operating personnel and management toward safety practices, there is still much ground to be covered.

To promote higher standards of safety performance, it is believed that safety education should be stressed more than ever before at the place of earliest training—in technical institutions, colleges, and universities—for it is from here that most industry leaders are recruited. This has been recognized by a number of educational institutions that are now incorporating safety training in their specialized engineering courses. Some of these have recommended advanced degrees in the field of professional safety engineering. This is believed to be a step in the right direction.

In view of this increased attention to safety training of students, it is hoped that this manual will be of use to college and university instructors. It is intended to serve as a guide to subject matter that could be covered in a series of lectures devoted to orienting students majoring in chemistry or chemical engineering. The material should not be regarded as a fixed code or set of regulations, but rather as a general guide for students seeking such information or for teachers who wish to inculcate fundamental knowledge of safety practices, and for institutional and laboratory directors.

Acknowledgment

This manual was prepared and sponsored by the General Safety Committee of the Manufacturing Chemists' Association, under the authorization of the Association's Board of Directors.

The Safety Committee drew upon their knowledge and experience for the text. Where material was furnished by outside sources, permission for reproduction was obtained from writers and publishers; full acknowledgment is given at appropriate places in the publication. The Association is also indebted to those who reviewed the manual prior to publication, many of whom made suggestions which were incorporated in the text.

The Committee recognizes that the unstinted efforts to put this manual in print represented an extracurricular activity for those taking part. Its completion reflects the excellent cooperation and safety-consciousness of individual members. To all contributors, the General Safety Committee, on behalf of the Association's Board of Directors, expresses its sincere gratitude.

Introduction

Briefly this Manual attempts to set forth:

1. A basis for guiding laboratory personnel, students, and teachers in good safety practices in the handling of hazardous chemicals.

2. General rules for the design and construction of a safe and efficient laboratory.

3. Equipment and service facilities that are necessary in properly designed laboratories.

4. Precautionary methods and personal protective equipment.

5. A description of hazards presented by certain physical and chemical properties of materials which possess fire, explosion, and health hazards, including precautions and safeguards.

6. First aid and suggested medical treatment of injuries resulting from exposure to chemicals.

7. References to sources of safety information, practical enough for use in training chemists and chemical engineers.

This manual is compiled primarily for college, university, and industrial chemical laboratory staff members, student bodies, and co-workers; however, there are several chapters which apply to high schools and elementary technical training schools where chemical laboratories are in existence or where chemicals may be handled.

Table of Contents

CHAPTER   PAGE

THE GENERAL SAFETY COMMITTEE iv

FOREWORD v

ACKNOWLEDGMENT vii

INTRODUCTION viii

I. GENERAL RULES FOR LABORATORY SAFETY . . . 1

II. LABORATORY DESIGN AND EQUIPMENT 7

III. HANDLING GLASSWARE 25

IV. HANDLING AND STORAGE OF CONTAINERS 38

V. MISCELLANEOUS HAZARDS 43

VI. FLAMMABILITY 52

VII. CHEMICAL HAZARDS 100

VIII. TOXICITY 125

IX. RADIATION SAFETY AND CONTAMINATION CONTROL
IN THE LABORATORY 146

X. PRESSURE VESSEL HAZARDS 162

XI. CLOTHING AND PERSONAL PROTECTIVE EQUIPMENT . 180

XII. LABORATORY FIRST AID AND SUGGESTIONS FOR MEDI-
CAL TREATMENT 193

XIII. THE PACKAGING AND TRANSPORTATION OF CHEMICALS 210

LITERATURE REFERENCES 217

INDEX 225

List of Plates

PLATE   PAGE

1. Completely fire-resistant structure with adequate nat-
    ural outside lighting. Doors with windows permit
    observation of approaching persons   8
2. Interior view of an analytical control laboratory, show-
    ing orderly arrangement of passageways, reagent bottles,
    lighting of individual sinks, hoods, and desk space . .   10
3. Section of a general laboratory illustrating ample pas-
    sageways, orderly arrangement, and good housekeeping   11
4. Laboratory designed for chemist and helper or two
    chemists   12
5. Location of hood away from outside wall, permitting
    natural lighting for room. All equipment arranged and
    placed so as not to obstruct passageway   13
6. Can for disposal of broken glass   14
7. A well ventilated laboratory with ample space for move-
    ment of personnel and location of apparatus . .   15
8. General laboratory showing one type of parallel service
    lines over the working benches, valves within easy reach,
    and plumbing over sinks   16
9. High-vacuum distillation apparatus erected on an open
    work bench, properly shielded to guard personnel . .   18
10. Hall of a building depicting utmost care in design and
    construction to safeguard employees engaged in work
    with hazardous chemicals   21
11. Tier of shelves portraying orderly classification and stor-
    age of glassware   26

PLATE   PAGE

12. Illustrating careful selection of correct glass apparatus
    and assembly for distillation and separation of purified
    fractions of organic materials   27
13. Illustration of one-unit titration apparatus showing re-
    agent shelf and correctly insulated wash bottle within
    reach of operator   28
14. Glass tubing being cut with the sharp edge of a file prior
    to breaking   29
15. Correct placement of hands around glass tubing to be
    broken   29
16. Glass tubing being cut with nichrome wire   31
17. Additional view of the cutting of glass tubing with
    nichrome wire   31
18. Proper method of freeing rubber stopper by use of cork
    borer   32
19. Appropriate and safe body, hand, and face protective
    equipment to be worn when cleaning dishes in strong
    acid or dichromate acid solution   35
20. Rack showing cleaned dishes which are subsequently
    removed when dry to proper lockers or drawers, leaving
    the rack free for other use   36
21. Cabinet for safe storage of flammable liquids   39
22. Wire shielding for protection of operator from flying
    glass in case of accidental breakage of infrared heating
    lamps   46
23. Protective face shield for work involving high-vacuum
    apparatus   47
24. Illustration of a well constructed hood for work with
    hazardous chemicals   48
25. Well arranged set used in fractionation of high boiling
    liquids or catalytic chemical reactions and subsequent
    separations of the end-products   49
26. Additional view of arrangement shown in Plate 25 (as
    seen from opposite end of room)   50
27. Examples of various radiation survey and monitoring
    instruments   160

PLATE   PAGE

28. Typical control panel installation of a high-pressure
    building 164
29. Batch-type autoclave capable of withstanding, and op-
    erating at, 2000 psi 169
30. Main control room in a high-pressure building for the
    operation of a continuous hydrogenation reaction . . 174
31. A corner of a Special Service Laboratory in which a
    range of research equipment is available 175
32. Group of buildings for hazardous operations . . . 176
33. Orderly pilot plant laboratory 177
34. Additional view of a pilot plant laboratory in which
    process development is conducted and control testing
    is underway 178
35. Protective clothing, and safeguards incorporated in the
    equipment in which radioactive measurements are un-
    derway 181
36. Flame-resistant garments, including head protection . 184
37. Respiratory protective equipment used in tank repair
    work 186
38. Method of handling dry ice 191
39. A typical first-aid room for medical treatment . . . 194

CHAPTER I

General Rules for Laboratory Safety

The persons in charge of chemical laboratories should be safety-minded. Their attitude toward fire and safety standard practices is invariably reflected in the behavior of their entire staff, because laboratory personnel are prone to emulate their supervisors.

Thus key men should:

1. Bear full responsibility for maintaining the highest standards of safe working conditions.
2. Provide safeguards against hazardous undertakings.
3. Educate their supervisory staffs to be alert to all hazards.

No general set of rules can ensure safety. Safety results from an attitude of mind and depends upon the effort of each individual to eliminate all unsafe conditions and acts that give rise to accidents. Positive action closes the door to potential dangers and reduces accidents to a minimum.

A safety program is only as strong as the worker's will to do the correct things at the right time. The fundamental weakness of most safety programs lies in too much lip service to safety rules and not enough action in putting them into practice.

Safety practices should be practical and enforceable. Management should avoid the tendency to place the blame for accidents on individuals, because many times the basic cause is its failure to select and train competent supervisory personnel and encourage the establishment of safe practices and working conditions.

A manufacturing plant cannot attain maximum efficiency in production unless each worker not only understands his duties, but also appreciates the other operations of the unit with which his job is integrated. So it is with safety; no worker operates as an entity. If he makes one false move resulting in an accident, he usually affects other parts of the operation.

This interdependence of all segments of a plant or laboratory emphasizes another fundamental of an effective safety program; the function of every tool, machine, and operation should be considered in relation to all others and coordinated into a unified plan that men, working diligently and intelligently, can carry out with maximum safety for the entire operation.

Most industrial, government, academic, and institutional laboratories have sets of safety regulations for their personnel. Differences in rules reflect differences in emphasis placed on certain sections of their codes, because hazards encountered differ with the location and nature of the work being performed.

Accident prevention is based on certain common standards of education, training of personnel, and provision of safeguards against accidents. To meet these standards, every laboratory should have:

1. A staff composed of safety-minded individuals.

2. A capable safety staff consisting of a safety group or committee, the leader or chairman of which should be the head of the laboratory or another person of substantial responsibility.

3. An educational program to promote safety and fire prevention.

4. Proper supervision of all work in various divisions of the laboratory by experienced men.

5. Regular inspection program of all working areas.

6. Corrective discipline for unsafe practices of laboratory personnel.

7. Adequate safeguards against physical exposure to hazardous chemicals and equipment.

8. A policy of encouraging the use of personal protective equipment, such as suitable clothing, eye protection, face shields, masks, etc.

9. First-aid facilities including competent personnel.

10. Complete records of all accidents for periodic computa-

tion of accident frequency and severity rates and for purposes to determine the causes of accidents and means of prevention.

In considering a program for laboratories—particularly a safety education program—the generally approved plan found in chemical plants is valuable. Such an organizational pattern is applicable to chemical laboratories, particularly the larger ones.

It would be difficult to describe an "average" or "typical" safety program in any chemical company. Some variation in safety programs is found from company to company and is based on differences in type of operation, size of plant, and size of the parent company in multi-unit operations. Program fundamentals, however, are remarkably similar in progressive companies regardless of the variables. Briefly they are outlined below.

FEATURES OF A REPRESENTATIVE SAFETY ORGANIZATION IN THE CHEMICAL INDUSTRY

A. Management participation in safety program.
  1. Declaration of company policy followed by executive personnel's continuing check on the program's progress.
B. Supervisory responsibility for employee safety.
  1. Each member of the supervisory staff held responsible for safety to the same extent that he is responsible for production, maintenance, or research, depending upon his specific assignment.
C. Assignment of staff function to safety personnel.
  1. Safety department, safety engineer, or other designated personnel given *recognition* and responsibility.
  2. Duties include correlation of accident-prevention activities, promoting the safety program, and advising management and supervisors regarding their safety problems.
D. Provision for safe working conditions—buildings and equipment.
  1. Establishment of engineering standards.
  2. Review of plans for new processes or equipment from safety and fire-protection engineering point of view.

3. Industrial hygiene surveys to evaluate potential chemical exposure hazards.

E. Safety education and safety training.
   1. Education of supervisory personnel to assist them in carrying out their assigned safety responsibilities.
   2. Employee education.
      a. New employee safety induction program organized on plant-wide (new employee) as well as departmental (new or transferred employee) basis.
      b. Specific job instruction designed to incorporate safe practices into operating instructions.
   3. Development of safety consciousness in all employees.
      a. Use of bulletins, posters, films, and other visual aids.
      b. Establishment of safety merit awards, contests, and similar interest-stimulating activities.

As a result of operations and materials-handling problems peculiar to the chemical industry, members of the Manufacturing Chemists' Association have found it desirable to stress certain phases of their safety programs. Much emphasis is placed on such phases as:

A. Employee training in first-aid measures for exposure to chemicals.
B. Periodic testing and inspection of pressure vessels and pressure relief devices.
C. Requirement of written permits for performing flame-producing work (welding or cutting) in locations where flammable liquids are stored or used.
D. Requirement for written permits authorizing vessel entry especially where the equipment has contained flammable, corrosive, or toxic materials.
E. Requirement that, during all hazardous operations involving flammable, toxic, or detonable materials, one or more individuals shall be within reasonable communicable distance of the operator.
F. Disposal of chemical wastes. In many instances, a separate department is established to handle technical and engineer-

TYPICAL PLANT SAFETY ORGANIZATION USED IN THE CHEMICAL INDUSTRY

Central or Plant Safety Committee

Department Safety Committee

Foreman's Safety Committee

*Safety Reprsentative: Assistance as required.
Usually attends meetings at Department level.
May not attend regularly at Foreman's level.

ing aspects of this problem. The problem is particularly close to chemical plant operation, and control measures are often correlated by engineering and safety personnel.

The accompanying chart blueprints the safety organization in the typical well-run chemical plant. As mentioned previously, the principles outlined above and incorporated into the chart are not unique with the chemical industry. Proper application of these principles in MCA member organizations has resulted in favorable industry-wide accident prevention experience. The organizational chart assumes the existence of safety committees, because committees have been found to be the most effective means of accomplishing the desired goal—enlisting each employee's personal effort toward preventing accidents.

CHAPTER II

Laboratory Design and Equipment

Since the design and facilities of laboratories are determined by the work carried on in them, only general rules for layout, construction, and equipment can be suggested. No matter what their function, however, all laboratories have in common many fundamental features which must be considered from a safety standpoint. Particular effort must be directed toward eliminating hazards and erecting safeguards to protect laboratory personnel.

Type of Construction

All laboratories should be of fire-resistant or noncombustible construction, depending on the degree of hazard the work entails. Combustible construction should never be used. (See the National Building Code, recommended by the National Board of Fire Underwriters, for different types of construction.)

Multiple-story buildings should have adequate means of exit, for example, two or more stairways so that the maximum distance to the nearest exit is not more than 75 feet for high-hazard activity and 100 feet for low-hazard work. For most laboratories, the 100-foot distance is sufficient.

All stairways are best enclosed with brick or concrete walls, or walls of other materials having structural strength and fire resistance adequate to withstand a moderate fire. It may be necessary to provide smokeproof stair towers if the work of the laboratory involves highly flammable or toxic materials. Exit doors at the entrance should swing out and approved Class B fire doors should be provided.

Every laboratory room should have adequate exit doors both

to permit quick, safe escape in an emergency and to protect the occupants from fires or accidents in adjoining rooms.

Because of the wide variety of operations, it is difficult to make specific recommendations, but some general principles are outlined here which have been found to be good practice in many laboratories.

In general, exit doors should swing outward. Occasionally, small rooms used for special laboratory work having little or no

Eastman Kodak Co.

Plate 1. Completely fire-resistant structure with adequate natural outside lighting. Note doors with window permitting observation of approaching persons.

hazard, such as photographic darkrooms, are safe with inward swinging doors, particularly where an outswinging door creates a hazard in itself.

Rooms for work of moderate hazard should have at least two doors, remotely located, if more than 10 persons regularly occupy the room. The number of persons should be reduced to 5 if there are hazardous operations, such as work with flammable liquids in appreciable quantities.

Check each room to make sure there is no chance of a person being trapped by fire, explosions, or release of dangerous gases between himself and a doorway.

Where a group of rooms enters a common hallway, one door may lead to a corridor, the second to an adjoining room. Often such an arrangement results in three doors in each room, one of which swings inward.

In hazardous laboratory operations, one door should lead to a corridor and the second door, directly outdoors. It is recommended that outswinging doors leading to corridors be recessed in vestibules so that the door will not swing out across the corridor, partly blocking it and creating a collision hazard.

Where more than 10 persons occupy a room and in high hazard situations, doors should be equipped with "panic" hardware.

Isolate highly hazardous areas by adequate fire walls. Openings in fire walls should be protected by fire doors properly equipped with fusible links for self-closure.

All laboratory rooms must have adequate ventilation to prevent build-up of highly flammable or toxic gases. Ventilating ducts should be run in fire-resistant shafts to block the spread of fire from floor to floor. Ducts should be equipped with automatic closing dampers where they enter the shaft.

Some work in the field of radioactivity (including biochemistry where radioactive elements are used as tracers) will probably prevent use of hollow types of construction for floors, exterior walls, and partitions, because it is difficult, if not impossible, to decontaminate such structures. (See Chapter IX.)

Ceiling lights should be ample (equivalent to normal daylight), otherwise personnel cannot work at maximum efficiency. Lighting installation must be in accordance with National Electrical Code.

There are many views regarding the need for windows in laboratories, but individual preference usually is the deciding factor. Outside windows provide the means for fresh-air supply and relieve the feeling of claustrophobia, but they present a problem of maintenance, periodic cleaning, etc. Many research laboratories have been built recently without windows and seem to be giving satisfactory service when light, heat, ventilation, and humidity are properly controlled. Laboratory rooms in which most of the work

Merck & Co., Inc.

Plate 2. Interior view of an analytical control laboratory. Note orderly arrangement of passageways, reagent bottles, lighting of individual sinks, hoods, and desk space.

is carried out with flammable liquids or gases should be provided with explosion-venting windows.

Layout of Furniture and Equipment

The proper arrangement of furniture in a laboratory requires much study so that available space is not wasted and resulting working conditions are efficient and safe.

Give first consideration to the provision of free escape in two directions for all aisles between benches, hoods, etc.; dead ends must be avoided.

Layouts provide, in some cases, two separate exits into corridors; in others, one escape into the corridor and another into an adjoining room. Again a "U" aisle around a central island bench and leading to a double-acting door may be adequate, especially if the work being carried on involves hazards of a lesser degree. Under all circumstances it is best to provide doors opening in the direction of egress.

Aisles between benches should be at least 4 feet wide to provide adequate room for passage of personnel and equipment.

Where desks abut benches, they should be separated by a safety shield, preferably of safety glass or equivalent, to protect the man at the desk from spills or explosions. Flammables are not to be kept on or under benches.

Where benches are placed back to back, there should be a center shield or barricade to protect workers on one side of a bench from possible spills, fires, or explosions on the other.

Private and other small laboratories should be designed for occupancy by at least two (chemist and helper or two chemists) if possible, especially when potentially dangerous work is to be performed.

Plate 3. Section of a general laboratory illustrative of ample passageways, orderly arrangement, and good housekeeping.

Monsanto Chemical Co.

Plate 4. Laboratory designed for chemist and helper or two chemists. Observe passageways, and exit, which is beyond sink and hood (left far corner) where hazardous work is underway.

Locate hoods on other than an outside wall so that natural light from windows is not obstructed.

Every laboratory should have an eye-wash station and a safety shower, readily accessible, preferably next to nearest exit or in swinging position over a sink. A deluge-type shower head with a quick opening valve, not spring-loaded, should be provided so that a person will have two hands free to remove his clothes while under the shower.

Do not put reagents on the shelving or racks at the rear of the bench, because there is danger of accident when the chemist reaches over apparatus for them. Receptacles are placed under the flasks containing flammable liquids, so that, in the event of break-

Plate 5. Location of hood away from outside wall, permitting natural lighting for room. All equipment is arranged and placed so as not to obstruct passageway.

age occurring over burners or heating elements, the resulting fires will be confined.

Separate storage for trash, waste chemicals, and broken glass should be provided (see Storage). Such waste should be removed from the building daily.

Hoods and Ventilation

Install hoods for all work with highly toxic or highly flammable materials.

All chemicals known to be highly toxic must be kept in closed containers and, if possible, prepared in closed equipment. These chemicals should be transferred to and from the containers inside exhaust hoods. The laboratory hoods should be large enough to permit complete enclosure of the equipment and operations.

It is recommended that hoods be constructed of noncombustible materials, with doors in the front, and ventilated so that both heavy and light fumes will be removed and will not enter the laboratory proper. Design should be such that the plenum chamber, ducts, and exhaust fan are easily accessible for cleaning.

American Cyanamid Co.

Plate 6. Can for disposal of broken glass.

Glazed doors with full-vision panels of laminated safety glass are recommended.

Vertical doors may be counterbalanced so that they can be raised or lowered easily and should stop 1 inch from the bottom to permit adequate ventilation.

Hoods should be ventilated separately, each having its own exhaust fan and duct with fans located so that the no-duct work is under pressure. To prevent return of contaminants to the building, the exhaust should be terminated at a safe distance from the building.

Make-up air should be supplied to rooms to replace the quantity of air exhausted through the hoods.

Hood ventilation systems are best designed to have an air flow of not less than 60 linear feet per minute across the face of the hood, with all doors open, and 150, if toxic materials are involved.

Exhaust fans should be spark-proof if exhausting flammable vapors, and corrosion-resistant if handling corrosive fumes.

Careful consideration should be given to the materials of construction for the exhausting equipment from the laboratory hoods through to the discharge points.

Plate 7. A well ventilated laboratory with ample space for movement of personnel and location of apparatus. Note floor service facilities for special experimental work.

Monsanto Chemical Co.

Monsanto Chemical Co.

Plate 8. General laboratory showing one type of parallel service lines over the working benches, valves within easy reach, and plumbing over sinks. Note sprinkler system on ceiling and adequate outside window lighting.

In multi-story buildings, vertical ducts should be installed within fire-resistant shafts and provided with fire dampers at all points where ducts pass through a shaft wall.

In installing laboratory ventilation, the NFPA standards for blower and exhaust systems must be followed.

Locate controls for all services at the front of the hood; they should be operable when the hood door is closed.

All laboratory rooms should have the air changed continuously, at a rate depending on the nature of the materials being handled.

Plumbing and Sinks

All services should be properly labeled. Service cocks should be installed with the outlets directed downward.

16

All laboratory benches should preferably have one sink to every two chemists. Equip each sink with hot and cold water taps, drain boards, and peg boards (which should not be used for storage). This equipment may be adequately supported by incombustible materials, protected against corrosive effects of laboratory chemicals.

Sinks should be of a nonabsorbent material resistant to chemicals used and produced in the laboratory.

It is desirable where relatively large quantities of phenolic wastes, or similar products, are handled to recommend that separate sinks with disposal traps be provided.

For drains, it is best to use chemically resistant material, the choice of material depending upon the nature of the experiments conducted. When a varied research program is carried on and the accompanying reactions are not readily predictable, Duriron is recommended. However, when the degree and type of corrosion are known to be not serious, cast iron may be considered.

Drains must be properly trapped and vented; they should be discharged into an industrial waste sewer, preferably not a sanitary sewer. Fixture traps should be of the same construction material as the drain. Fill traps with water to prevent toxic fumes from spreading to adjacent drainage systems.

A safety shower and eye-wash equipment should be standard equipment of every laboratory. Floors around safety showers should slope toward the location of floor drains.

Special gases should be piped to the benches from cylinders equipped with proper valves and controls, and located in a special closet reserved outside the laboratory building for them. Location outside blank (masonry) walls is preferable. Where this is not practicable, limit the size of the cylinder to one that can be placed inside the fume hood.

Electrical Layout

Electrical layouts for buildings and laboratories invariably are incorporated into the basic designs and must adhere to prescribed codes, either local or national. Although some of the most important rules are given here, it is best to rely on competent per-

Plate 9. High-vacuum distillation apparatus erected on an open work bench, properly shielded to guard personnel.

Lederle Lab. Div., American Cyanamid Co.

sonnel who know and will follow prescribed local, state, and national codes in installing electrical facilities in a given laboratory.

Place electrical outlets outside of the hood to afford easy access and thus protect them from spills and corrosion by gases.

All extension cords should be of the three-pole type to provide for adequate grounding. For work involving flammable liquids, plugs which can be de-energized before removal from receptacles should be used. Noninterchangeable plugs should be provided for multiple electrical services.

Equipment Safeguards

All moving mechanical equipment must be properly guarded to prevent injury to operators.

Work involving high-pressure autoclaves and bombs should be performed within properly barricaded stalls or rooms with outside controls, or outside barricade with vision port for operation from outside position. When working with very small bombs, portable shields may be adequate (see Chapter X on Pressure Vessels).

Storage

In the layout of each laboratory room adequate storage space and facilities should be provided for mechanical equipment and glassware which will be used regularly. These requirements will undoubtedly vary widely both with the kind of work being done and the over-all size of the laboratory force and the space allotted to it.

In the smaller laboratories where the number of rooms and the technical men employed do not justify central storerooms and service facilities, the amount of space allotted to each laboratory room must, of necessity, be greater because sufficient shelves, drawers, and cabinets must be provided in each room to permit the storage of practically all the mechanical equipment and glassware used by the workers in the room. Overstocking, however, should be avoided.

As the number of individual laboratory rooms increases, it

becomes more economical to reduce each laboratory's shelving, drawers, and cabinets to the minimum necessary for the equipment in current use. Consideration may then be given to a centralized storeroom where mechanical equipment, such as large or specialized types of glassware, is pooled. The choice of items to be pooled can only be made after a thorough study of the activities of the laboratory as a whole. Examples to be considered for pooling in a central storeroom would include voltage regulators, mantle heaters, vacuum pumps, pH meters, glass apparatus with ground tapered joints, unusual glassware not in regular use, and even such common items as ring stands, clamps, etc.

Setting up central storage where items may be checked in and out as needed simplifies the storage and housekeeping problems of the individual laboratory rooms and permits substantial economies through lower inventories and economical buying. It also provides storage space for standard volumetric solutions for the analytical personnel.

Storage of chemicals within the laboratory room will also vary with the type of chemical work being done; however, certain general principles can be followed. For the most part, stock reagents are best stored on open shelves within easy reach. The largest containers should be stored on the bottom shelves. It is recommended that strongly corrosive materials be stored in lead trays as near the floor level as possible. Trays should be deep enough to hold contents of bottles if leakage should occur.

Whether a molding or lip is needed on the edge of shelves to prevent reagent bottles from sliding off is debatable, but where vibration levels are high this practice is safer.

Flammable solvents should preferably not be stored in glass bottles over 1 liter in size. Large quantities should be stored in metal safety cans. Quantities requiring containers larger than 1 gallon should be stored outside the laboratory.

Where outside solvent rooms are provided it is essential that the area be well ventilated to avoid accumulation of escaping vapors from accidental spills or leakages. All lighting and electrical wiring should conform with the National Electrical Code. The large containers should be provided with breather vents, self-

Plate 10. Hall of a building depicting utmost care in design and construction to safeguard employees engaged in work with hazardous chemicals. Note correct lighting, placement of showers, fire extinguishers, visibility of exit doors, etc.

closing faucets, drip pans, etc. Suitable fire protection must be installed. This includes fire extinguishers and automatic sprinkler system as prescribed by the NFPA Code.

If a domestic refrigerator is provided for storage or cooling of small samples of flammable liquids, all electrical equipment should be removed from the storage box.

Cylinders of compressed or liquefied gases exceeding 1 pint capacity should not be stored in the laboratory room.

Gases under pressure and low boiling liquids should not be stored close to a source of heat, such as a radiator or hot plate. Whenever possible cylinders of compressed gases, if stored out-of-doors, should be shaded from direct sunlight, particularly during hot weather.

A conveniently located room (preferably cool location) equipped with adequate shelving can be set up as a central storeroom, with a competent clerk in charge. Through such an arrangement, chemists may store chemicals not in current use.

Housekeeping

Housekeeping plays an important role in reducing the frequency of laboratory accidents. Rooms should be kept in a neat, orderly condition. Floors, shelves and tables should be kept free from dirt and from all apparatus and chemicals not in use.

A cluttered laboratory is a dangerous place to work. Maintenance of a clean and orderly work space is indicative of interest, personal pride, and safety-mindedness. If one cleans up after each step in an experiment, or while waiting for the completion of another, general housecleaning is necessary only occasionally.

All of the passageways should be kept clear to all building exits and stairways. Space around emergency safety showers, eyewash stations, fire extinguishers, and electrical controls must be kept free from obstruction at all times. When apparatus is set up, it should be placed well back from the front edge of the desk. Ice, stirring rods, stoppers, borings from stoppers, etc., should be picked up from the floor immediately so as to prevent falls.

Water outlets should be turned off except when in actual use. Hoses should be securely fastened to equipment when water is left running, especially when experiments are unattended. Bunsen burners should not be left burning when not in use. Valves should be turned off on all inactive compressed air and vacuum lines.

Spilled mercury must be cleaned up at once. When left in crevices it may produce traces of mercury vapor or generate suspended droplets in the air and thus create a continuous cumulative hazard. Mercury droplets may be collected by using a hose connected to a heavy walled flask under vacuum. Mercury which cannot be picked up in this manner may be made safe by dusting with powdered zinc or powdered sulfur. Avoid ignition of sulfur dust.

Metal containers should be provided for the disposal of broken glassware. Such containers may be placed at strategic locations in laboratory corridors for disposing of broken glassware and should be properly labeled.

Separate approved waste disposal cans, stoneware crocks, or enamel buckets should be provided for the disposal of waste chemicals. Flammable liquids not miscible with water and corrosive materials, or compounds which are likely to give off toxic vapors (such as hydrogen cyanide), should never be poured into the sink. Do not mix reactive chemicals with waste solvents.

Dilute acids and alkalies may be disposed of by flushing them down the sink with a large quantity of cold water. Other miscellaneous waste should be disposed of by placing it in waste cans specifically provided for this purpose, never in wastebaskets.

Fire Protection

In considering fire protection, it should not be taken for granted that because laboratory personnel are technically trained they are familiar with the fire hazards existing in chemical work, particularly research. It is expected that they familiarize themselves with fire prevention rules and ways to combat fires in case one occurs. (See Chapter VI.)

Basic to reduction of fire hazards is the proper choice of materials of construction, adequate means of exit, adequate space between benches, etc., as discussed under "Layout of Furniture and Equipment" and "Type of Construction."

Automatic sprinkler systems are an accepted means of controlling fires in chemical laboratories.

Ventilation alone may not afford sufficient protection in hoods where highly flammable liquids are employed. Such operations may require an automatic or manually operated CO_2 extinguishing system, including automatic stopping of fans and closing of doors to prevent escape of the CO_2 gas.

First-aid fire extinguishers should be provided at convenient locations, one unit for every 2500 square feet of floor area or for each laboratory if the work carried on involves handling of flammables (see Chapter VI). If there are, in the laboratory, toxic materials which present a fire risk, it is preferable to locate the extinguisher outside of the room so that a worker won't have to be exposed to noxious fumes to get an extinguisher. Locating extinguishers at doorways to laboratories is desirable.

Standpipe systems and hose protection with spray nozzles should be located at or near the entrance to laboratories so that they may be readily available in case of fire.

Isolation of some hazardous work may be necessary, in which case the operation should be cut off adequately with fire walls. Door openings in the walls should be provided with approved automatic closing doors.

Openings around piping and equipment which pierce floors should be filled to prevent spread of fire from floor to floor. Where numerous pipe lines pierce floors, it may be well to fill in with vermiculite-concrete which can be readily removed.

Alarms

An approved fire alarm system with enough gongs to alert all occupants should be provided. It is recommended that such system should be connected to a central station when necessary.

Wherever a hazard of accidental release of toxic gases exists, a gas alarm system to warn occupants to evacuate the building should be provided. Gas masks of oxygen or compressed air type should be located near exits, and selected personnel trained to use them in case rescue work should become necessary (see Chapter XII).

CHAPTER III

Handling Glassware

Most chemical laboratory work involves the use of glassware, and glass breaks easily. Therefore, laboratory personnel must guard against being casual in handling glassware and always treat it with the care it requires. Vigilance in the selection and use of glass equipment can prevent breakage and subsequent injury from broken glass, and the contents of the equipment, or, in the case of unavoidable rupture of glass equipment, can prevent the accident from having serious consequences.

Receiving, Inspection, Storage

Shipments of glassware should be examined and their contents checked against the vendor's marking for correct storage. Manufacturer's or supplier's catalog numbers serve as satisfactory guides for identifying the ware. Packages should be piled so as not to impose excessive weight on the lower containers. Store glassware so as to permit removal without risk of breakage.

Each package containing glassware should be opened and inspected for cracked or nicked pieces, pieces with flaws that may become cracked in use, and badly shaped pieces. Such rejects, if not returned to the supplier, must be disposed of in an approved receptacle. All packing materials should be removed from each piece before storing.

Store glassware on well-lighted stockroom shelves designed for this purpose and having a coping of sufficient height around the edges to prevent the pieces from falling off. These rules should be followed:

Plate 11. Tier of shelves portraying orderly classification and storage of glassware. Each nest contains only one category of ware, thus making for ready location.

Lederle Lab. Div., American Cyanamid Co.

1. Store heavy pieces on lower shelves, light pieces on upper shelves. Store tall pieces at the back, smaller ones toward the front of the shelf.

2. Store glassware no higher than a person can easily reach without standing on a stepladder or something even more dangerous such as a box, shelf, etc.

3. Store glass tubing and rods in a horizontal position with no piece protruding over the coping.

4. Store delicate pieces in separate cartons clearly marked for ready identification.

As in the case of the laboratory proper, keep aisles between shelves in the storeroom clear of obstacles and debris at all times.

Plate 12. This setting depicts careful selection of correct glass apparatus and assembly for distillation and separation of purified fractions of organic materials. Note the alignment of heating elements, hose, rubber stopper, and clamp connections.

E. I. du Pont de Nemours & Co., Inc.

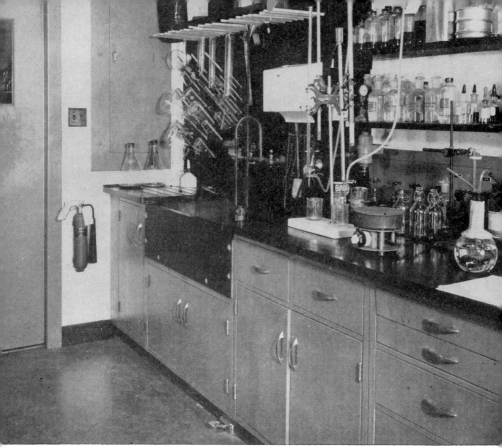

Plate 13. Illustration of one-unit titration apparatus showing necessary re-agent shelf and correctly insulated wash bottle within reach of operator. Note the accessibility of small fire extinguisher and properly designed swinging door.

Selection of Glassware

The piece of glassware that is designed for the type of work planned is the one to select. For pressures slightly above normal, pressure bottles should be chosen; for filtration with the aid of suction, vacuum flasks. Each piece should be inspected before use. Types of glass rods and tubing can be identified by refraction in a medium of carbon tetrachloride and benzene by comparison with approved standards.

Setting Up Apparatus

Apparatus (a combination of two or more units) is set up with the units in line and adequately supported by clamps on stands so

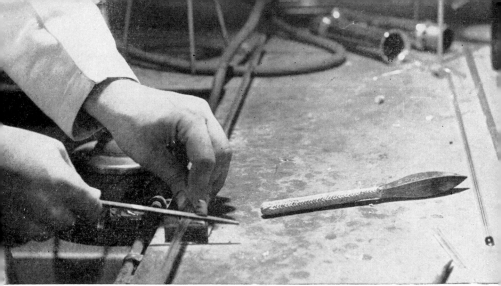

Plate 14. Glass tubing being cut with the sharp edge of a file prior to breaking, as indicated in Plate 15.

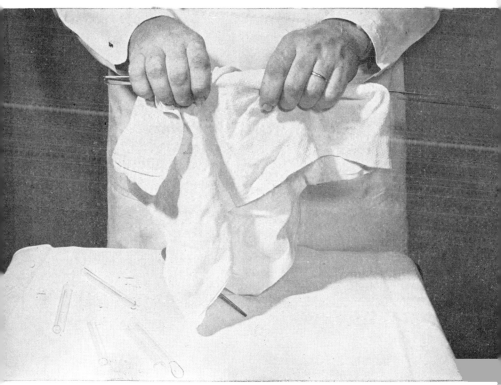

Plate 15. Correct placement of hands around glass tubing to be broken at chosen place.

that no unit exerts a strain on another unit. Laminated safety glass protective shields are placed around the apparatus to protect workers on both sides of the bench, if necessary.

Cutting Tubing and Rods

To cut glass tubing or a rod, make a straight clean cut with a cutter at the point where the piece is to be severed. Place a towel over the piece to protect the hands and fingers; then break away from the body. Make the break by placing the fingers around the piece with the thumbs together opposite the cut and bend toward the body.

Large-size tubing is cut by means of a nichrome wire looped around the piece at the point of severance. The wire should be heated electrically with a rheostat in the circuit. When the wire around the glass is hot, a drop of water is placed along the wire, thus causing the glass to break. Cut ends of glass tubing or rod are then fire polished.

Glass and Rubber or Cork Connections

When it is necessary to insert a piece of glass tubing or a rod through a perforated rubber or cork stopper, select the correct bore so that the insertion can be made without excessive strain. The glass and/or stopper should be wet (water or glycerine). Hold the stopper in the fingers of one hand and insert the glass by rotating and pushing with the fingers of the other hand placed near the end being inserted. Keep the hands out of the line of the end of the glass being pushed through the hole. Pay careful attention to this procedure when working with bent glass tubing. It is always best to wear leather or cotton gloves, or wrap a towel around the palms of the hands. Bear in mind that leather gloves are preferable.

Another good method of positioning glass tubing in rubber stoppers is to use the borer as a guide. Merely insert the borer in the stopper, position it along the tube, and then remove the borer.

It is occasionally necessary to remove a glass tube or a rod that is stuck to a rubber stopper. Sometimes it can be separated by

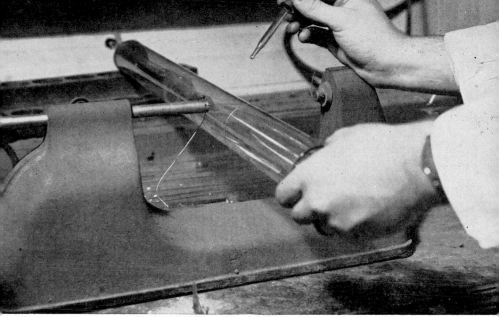

Plate 16. Glass tubing being cut with nichrome wire. Note the dropper which provides a drop of water of sufficient size to complete the job.

Plate 17. A second view of cutting glass tubing with nichrome wire. Note electric button switch on cutting block.

rolling the stopper with a block of wood under enough pressure to flex the rubber. If the glass tubing is straight, a brass cork borer that will fit neatly around the tube can be used to cut the rubber and free it. If it is very difficult to free the tube, it may be preferable to scrap the stopper and tube.

Rubber stoppers or corks are appropriately selected to fit the opening into which they are to be inserted and of correct density to make a tight closure without undue pressure. Use the fingers and not the hands when making this insertion.

Choose rubber tubing to fit glass connections snugly, with the end of the rubber cut at an angle so that it will stretch easily. To make connections, grip the glass piece close to its end with the fingers, keeping the hands out of its line. Wetting of the glass will expedite insertion (water or glycerine).

Plate 18. Proper method of freeing rubber stopper by use of cork borer. Under adverse conditions, protect hands by using gloves or towel.

Lederle Lab. Div., American Cyanamid Co.

Heating of Glassware

Usually flasks are best heated by electric mantles, particularly when flammable liquids are involved. Glassware to be heated by an open flame should be rested on a nichrome wire gauze or iron wire mesh with an asbestos center to prevent the flame from coming into contact with the glass above the level of the liquid being heated. This will avoid cracking of the vessel.

Confining Glassware

Pressure flasks which are to be heated under temperature control, as by a water bath or electric oven, must be shielded so that, in the event the flask is ruptured, its contents and fragments of broken glass will be safely deflected.

Pressure Relief for Glassware

Pressure should be released from, or applied to, glass vessels slowly.

Provide a pressure control valve or a water column trap installed between a cylinder of compressed gas and a glass vessel into which the gas is to be conducted.

An empty flask, bottle, or suitable surge-equalizing container can be installed where there is likely to be a change in pressure that might cause liquid in one vessel to flow into another and create a hazardous reaction or condition.

Pressurizing Glassware

It is generally unsafe to put pressure on laboratory glassware to expel its contents. An exception is the use of the laboratory wash bottle where only light pressure is applied. Liquids may be transferred by pouring or syphoning.

Outage in Bottles

Fill reagent and other bottles to not more than three fourths of their capacity at room temperature, leaving one fourth of the capacity as outage to allow for expansion.

Carrying Containers

Severe vibration of a vacuum container may result in a collapse, equivalent to the shattering effect of an explosion. But if absolutely necessary to move them while under vacuum, vacuum desiccators may be transported in a wooden box or metal shield.

Carry beakers and all usual shapes of flasks and bottles with the fingers around the body of the vessel. Do not grasp or hold by the lip or edge.

Hold volumetric and other long-neck flasks at both top and bottom when their contents are being agitated.

When examining the contents of glassware by light from above, the laboratory worker should hold the vessel at a safe distance and height to avoid injury to the head and eyes in case some of the contents should spill or the vessel should slip out of control.

Transport all bottles in standard carriers; no more than can be carried conveniently should be taken at one time.

Special metal or plastic containers should be used to transport bottles of acids, alkalies, or other corrosive or flammable liquids, the capacity of the container being sufficient to hold the contents of the bottles if they should break.

For construction of the container, select a material resistant to the chemical to be transported.

Labeling Bottles

All reagent bottles and other containers of laboratory chemicals, samples, and other materials, must be clearly labeled. A coat of clear lacquer applied to the label will protect it. (See MCA Manual L-1, *Warning Labels* for recommended nomenclature for labels.)

Reagent Shelves

Double-sided reagent shelves require a center partition high enough to prevent the pushing off of a bottle from one side by pressure from the opposite side.

Glass flasks, empty or containing clear liquids, should be

Plate 19. Appropriate and safe body, hand, and face protective equipment to be worn when cleaning dishes in strong acid or dichromate acid solution. Note hood and air duct over acid basin and wire basket for immersion into and lifting of glass from the acid bath.

Commercial Solvents Corp.

Plate 20. Rack showing cleaned dishes. After drying these are usually removed to proper lockers or drawers, leaving the rack free for other use.

placed where the sun's rays cannot fall upon them. This will avoid potential fires.

Large bottles of acids, alkalies, or other corrosive liquids are not to be placed on shelves above head level. Reagent or solution bottles provided with delivery tubes can be secured so that they cannot be tipped when the contents are being withdrawn.

Cleaning Glassware

Before turning glassware over to another person to be thoroughly cleaned for storage, the user must see that each piece is free of any material that might cause a hazard.

The user must clean any apparatus which may require special

treatment because of the material it may contain, or because of its design and construction.

In washing glassware, no more than gentle pressure should be applied in wiping the inside. Excessive pressure may cause jagged sections to split off. The washer should wear rubber gloves to prevent cuts and skin damage from chemical irritants. The use of a mixture of trisodium phosphate and pumice, or other mild cleaners or equivalent, is preferred to strong acid or caustic.

Correctly designed brushes are always used to clean glassware. Worn brushes should be discarded, because the metal portions of the brush may scratch the glass.

Broken Glass Disposal

To remove glass splinters from a sink or other area, use a whiskbroom and a dustpan. Very small pieces can be picked up with a large piece of wet cotton.

Provide a separate specially marked receptacle for broken glassware. Broken glassware must be kept out of baskets or containers of wastepaper, rags, and other discarded materials.

Glass Stoppers

In this manual, no great emphasis will be placed on a safe procedure for removing stuck (frozen) glass stoppers in bottles. This was a frequent hazard years ago, but now a commercially available dependable bottle stopper remover has been developed and is recommended.

Special Hazards

Special hazards are encountered in handling explosives, oxidizing materials, poisonous substances, radioactive materials and extremely flammable solvents in glassware, as in other equipment. In such instances, specific precautions should be formulated for the guidance of the laboratory technicians. Bacteriological laboratories and those designed for other work presenting special hazards also require special procedures in handling glassware (see Chapter VII)

CHAPTER IV

Handling and Storage of Containers

Containers used in the chemical laboratory, other than shelf-reagent bottles, include any box, carton, crate, cylinder, or drum in which reagents and equipment are shipped or stored.

In general, the exercise of good judgment and careful manipulation, coupled with adequate information and vigilant supervision, will eliminate any physical hazard in handling and storing containers. All must be handled with as much care in the laboratory as in the plant. A broken toe or a mashed foot can incapacitate a worker for weeks or months, and a sliver or small scratch or cut, if not attended to promptly, may become infected and result in serious illness. The following suggestions, if followed, will help prevent such accidents:

1. Wear serviceable gloves and safety shoes.

2. Make sure you know the safe way to lift; keep your back straight, and lift with your leg muscles.

3. Never lift a package of any sort without some idea of how heavy it is. Get help for lifting heavy loads.

4. Look out for slivers, projecting nails, sharp wires, and strap ends on packages being handled.

5. Get a good grip on the package, and watch your step.

6. Don't store pasteboard or fiber boxes in damp or wet places. When a full box of such construction is picked up, the bottom may easily give way if wet.

7. When trucking bottles, remember that small-bottle crates should not be piled more than three high on hand trucks; 5-gallon bottle crates should not be more than two high. Small-bottle crates should not overhang.

Plate 21. One type of cabinet useful for safe storage of flammable liquids.
Note type of cans, nature of space and ventilation (on top of shelf area).
When cabinet is closed and a leak should occur, vapors will be carried off.

8. Do not overload trucks, wheelbarrows, or elevators. Handle all chemical package crates cautiously; inspect to make sure crate has not been damaged and chemicals spilled.

Cylinders

Cylinders of $4\frac{1}{2}$-inch diameter can be supported by a base support made of welded pipe. The larger cylinders must be securely fastened so that they cannot be dislodged or tipped in any direction. Chains or clamps, connected to an adjacent wall or structural member, are suitable for this.

1. All cylinders should be checked for correct labeling before use. Cylinders of compressed gases must never be stored near flame, electric hot plates, steam pipes, or other sources of radiant heat.

2. Cylinders containing flammable gases such as hydrogen or acetylene should not be used near open flames.

3. Empty cylinders or cylinders not in use should not be stored in laboratory rooms, but should be returned to the storeroom.

4. The valves on empty cylinders should be kept securely closed to prevent admixture of air with the next filling charge.

5. Connections, gauges, regulators, or fittings used with other cylinders must not be interchanged with oxygen cylinder fittings because of the possibility of fire or explosion from a reaction between oxygen and residual oil in the fitting.

6. Cylinders should be used in the correct position to ensure that the proper phase is delivered at the valve.

7. A trap should be inserted in outlet lines to prevent liquid from flowing back into cylinders. If the liquid phase is being delivered from the cylinder, a trap will not permit return but a check valve will.

8. When it is necessary to heat a cylinder of liquefied gas to obtain an adequate flow of gas, follow the specific recommendation of the supplier for the particular gas. Storing it in a warm room for several hours often suffices. Never use heat from gas burners, torches, or electricity; one reason is that the safety device

may function and suddenly discharge the contents of the cylinder.

9. Pressure regulators are used with cylinders of compressed gases to maintain a desired pressure for laboratory use. Although these regulators seldom require repairs if properly used, they are easily damaged when misused, and misuse will very likely occur when an uninformed person attempts to operate them.

10. No person should attempt to operate a pressure regulator without instruction.

It is essential that dirt and oil be kept out of regulators; that regulators not be subjected to sudden pressure change, falls, or shock; and that the back pressure be kept below the delivery pressure on the low-pressure side. It is also essential that oxygen regulators not be used for combustible gases, or vice versa; also that regulator valves for chlorine cylinders not be interchanged with regulators for other gases.

Some detailed precautions for operating pressure regulators are:

(a) Do not use oil on regulators or cylinder valve.

(b) Blow dust out of the cylinder valve by opening the valve and closing it quickly before attaching regulator. This method is not recommended for hydrogen or toxic gas cylinders.

(c) Use the proper wrench (not pipe wrench) to attach the regulator.

(d) Do not interchange oxygen regulators and combustible gas regulators or interchange chlorine regulator valve with any other. Authorization should be obtained before interchanging regulators for any gases.

(e) Release pressure-adjusting screw by turning it to the left before opening cylinder valve.

(f) Open the cylinder valve slowly, watching the high-pressure gauge closely. When the hand starts to move, close cylinder valve slightly, manipulating valve so that the pressure rises slowly. When pressure reaches a maximum, open cylinder valve fully.

(g) When using oxygen, never move the pressure-adjusting screw while the hose-outlet valve is closed. It is essential that a vent for excess back pressure to escape be provided; that is, the pressure on the inner side of the low-pressure diaphragm must be greater than the back pressure in the hose.

(h) Keep flames away from cylinders and regulators.

(i) Keep caps on cylinders when not in use.

(j) Store all fittings where they will remain clean.

(k) Pressure should not be left on regulators when not in use.

Manifolds

Manifolds should be installed strictly in accordance with supplier's recommendations.

Drums

Although seldom used by the laboratory worker, drums present a physical hazard. The following precautions should be followed:

1. Drums should never be filled to capacity. Sufficient outage (vapor space) must be allowed for expansion of the liquid. Do not put under pressure to remove contents.

2. Spark-resistant tools should always be used on drums containing flammable liquids.

3. A drum should be rolled by exerting a force against the side of the drum with the hands. Never attempt to push or change the direction of a rolling drum with the feet.

4. Drums should be handled only with ropes or other tackle when raising or lowering them from one level to another on inclines or skids.

5. Do not stand in the way of a moving drum or place any portion of the body under an incline or skid. Bungs should be securely tightened before moving the drum.

6. Drum storage racks should be designed so that each drum is held firmly in place to eliminate rolls and falls.

7. To remove the hazard of static electricity, all racks and drums used for storage of flammable liquids should be grounded. (Refer to MCA Drum Manuals.)

8. Drum pumps are recommended for removing flammable liquid contents.

CHAPTER V

Miscellaneous Hazards

Nonchemical Burns

Nonchemical burns can be avoided by preventing accidental contact with hot solids, liquids, and gases. Relatively minor burns are frequently caused by forgetfulness or undue haste in picking up hot objects with bare hands, or in brushing against heated equipment with the body. Uninsulated steam lines, even the small sections of metal tubing used to heat water or oil baths, frequently cause minor burns. Burns also can result from lighting Bunsen burners and other flame generating equipment.

Most thermal burns can be avoided by using tongs or asbestos gloves when handling hot objects, and closing match boxes or packages before striking matches on them (or better still by using flint gas lighters in place of friction matches).

Extremely cold materials, such as liquid nitrogen, liquid air, solid carbon dioxide, and various compressed gases will produce frostbite which is slow to heal.

Ladders and Tools

A straight ladder should be placed so that its foot is at a distance of one fourth the length of the ladder from the wall or building; thus a 12-foot ladder should be placed so that its foot is 3 feet from the wall it leans against. Ladders should be tied or otherwise firmly fastened in position, or steadied by another man. Ladders and their use should conform to ASA Standards.

43

Hand Tools

In fitting pipe or tightening a bolt, a worker using the wrong size wrench can sustain an injury ranging from a skinned knuckle to a broken hand, a strained back, or a serious fall if the tool slips. To prevent this, only wrenches that fit the job should be used and, like all tools, they should be kept in good condition.

The two types of hammers in everyday use, the carpenter's hammer and the machinist's hammer, should not be interchanged in their applications. The face of the carpenter's hammer should be flat and parallel to the axis of the handle, but the machinist's hammer more beveled or rounded at the edges to decrease any tendency to mushroom. In driving nails, a flat face will help to prevent the hammer from slipping off the head of the nail or causing the nail to fly; hence it should be properly faced.

Fitting a hammer handle to the head has a lot to do with its safe use. Hammers with split or damaged handles should not be used.

Any kind of hand tool, whether a wrench, hammer, drill, saw, screwdriver, chisel, or knife, should be manipulated in such a way that the body will not be injured if the tool should slip. For example, one should cut away from the body, not toward it; both hands should be kept above or behind the cutting edge of the tool. Another common laboratory tool, the cork-borer, should be used so that as it emerges from the cork the hand cannot be cut.

Electrical Hazards

Electrical service lines in the laboratory can be the source of serious accidents. A person standing on a floor, which is wet or otherwise well grounded, is in danger of carrying current and getting a severe shock through his entire body if his hand touches electrical equipment that has been energized. Before manipulating electrical equipment, particularly 110-volt or higher, such as rheostats or switches, even if thought to be well insulated, one should see that his hands are dry and that he is standing on a dry nonmetallic spot (preferably a rubber mat), and then be sure that he grasps the equipment at a properly insulated point.

Brine-soaked floors have a high conductivity and constitute particularly hazardous grounds. In operations involving step-down transformers, it is exceedingly important that they be connected properly to the line; for if the secondary were mistakenly connected to the line, the voltage would be stepped up rather than down and the operator could easily be electrocuted on accidental contact with the resulting high potential.

Metal cases of electrical equipment must be connected to ground. Portable equipment should be provided with three conductor cables or supplementary ground.

Never start an electric motor without making sure that no one is in a position where he might be injured.

In making electric connections in the laboratory, cotton-covered wire, such as ordinary lamp cord, should never be used because of the possibility of its becoming water-soaked and thereby presenting an extra shock hazard. Use only properly insulated wire.

Temporary wiring should be secured overhead, rather than on the floor where it might cause tripping.

Brine Lines

Cooling brine service lines as used in the laboratory require intelligent operation to hold leaks, stoppages, and repairs to a minimum. Brine lines not in use should be left with both the high-pressure and low-pressure outlet valves closed, but with the by-pass valve open so that the brine can circulate and be less likely to settle out in the pipes and cause stoppages. (However, it is often necessary to keep lower floor by-pass valves closed to maintain adequate pressure on upper floors.)

In starting brine flowing through a low-pressure system, such as a glass condenser connected with rubber tubing, close the brine by-pass valve, slowly open the low-pressure brine outlet valve until it is wide open, and finally open the high-pressure brine outlet valve slowly and just sufficiently to produce an adequate flow through the system. If the by-pass is left open, or if the high-pressure brine outlet valve is opened wide, the tubing or the glass condenser may burst under the pressure.

Esso Research Center, Standard Oil Development Co.

Plate 22. Illustration of wire shielding for protection of operator from flying glass in case of accidental breakage of infrared heating lamps.

Where possible, brine pipe and fittings should be of all-iron construction. Where copper tubing is used, it should be braced so that it will not be weakened and broken by flexing.

Tubing used to carry brine should be capable of resisting considerable pressure; red rubber tubing, or heavy walled black rubber tubing as used for vacuum work, is satisfactory. Flexible tubing in brine service must be clamped firmly with a turn of wire where it joins the supply valves, condenser outlets, or other connections. Monel wire is recommended for this purpose because it possesses satisfactory corrosion resistance and mechanical strength. The operator should be careful to fold down sharp projecting ends of the wire.

Spilled calcium chloride brine is corrosive and irritating to

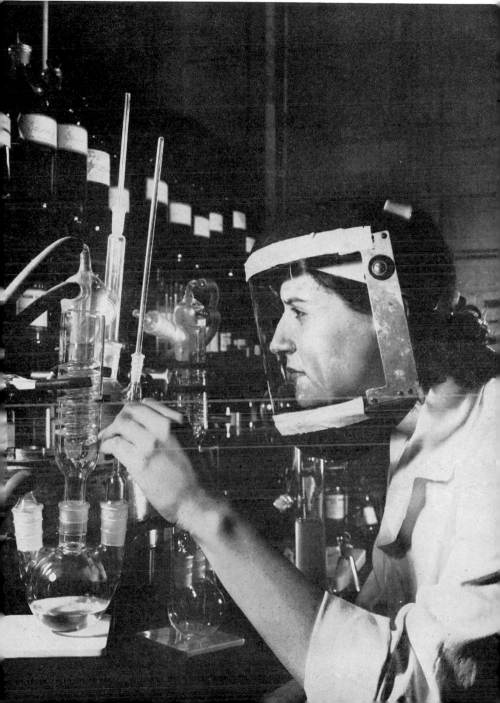

Plate 23. Protective face shield useful in working with high-vacuum apparatus.

Merck & Co., Inc.

The Dow Chemical Co.

Plate 24. Illustration of a well constructed hood for work with hazardous chemicals. This shows good lighting and orderly arrangement of apparatus. The shatter-proof glass, metal-framed sliding doors are excellent for partial closure (three sections) to facilitate ventilation.

the skin, difficult to clean up, and easily damages electrical equipment. Other refrigerants may be combustible or toxic. Exercise care to avoid brine leaks; brine conduit made of flexible tubing or glass parts should always be turned off at the valve when unattended (as at night). Avoid brine leakage on any electrical connections; short circuits and consequent fires may result.

Miscellaneous

Liquids of any kind on the floor increase the hazard of slips and falls.

Cloths used to mop up spilled flammable liquids should be

Plate 25. Well arranged set used in fractionation of high boiling liquids or catalytic chemical reactions and subsequent separations of the end products.

Plate 26. Another view of the same arrangement shown in Plate 25 (as seen from opposite end of room).

dampened before use, soaked in water immediately afterward, and disposed of in a manner which will avoid fires.

Halls, aisles, and passageways to exits should be kept open and uncluttered. Do not store combustible materials in exit passageways.

Finger rings are objectionable because they can easily catch on projections and cause the fingers to be injured; also they tend to hold chemicals, thus aggravating the action of skin irritants.

Where there is danger of bumping, stones, glass beads, or fragments should be added to liquids which are to be heated. They should be added well below the boiling temperature of the liquid. If a liquid is inadvertently heated without them, do not add the stones until the liquid has been sufficiently cooled, otherwise violent ebullition may occur.

Bad falls may sometimes result from leaning too far back in chairs, particularly in swivel chairs.

Do not open casement windows by pushing against the glass, for if the glass breaks a bad cut may result.

Do not transport flammable, toxic, or corrosive materials by elevator while it is carrying passengers. Such materials, if not in the original sealed packages, should be conveyed only in safety containers. Open containers must never be employed.

Going up and down stairs with arms overloaded with flammable or toxic materials in glassware may result in serious falls. One hand should always be free to hold to the rail, and only small quantities should be carried at a time, with the glassware held in a large leak-proof container.

CHAPTER VI

Flammability

Flammable Materials

Whenever a new chemical is synthesized or isolated, or a novice comes in contact for the first time with any flammable chemical, the potential danger of fire exists. It is therefore essential that chemical and physical properties of new materials be determined, those of other chemicals be studied and well understood.

In the case of a known product, textbooks, handbooks, or other references will give the essential information required for determining the proper safety precautions to be taken. However, for a new chemical all requisite properties must be determined in routine laboratory procedure.

The following facts should be known for the safe handling of a given chemical:

1. Physical state of the product. Is it a liquid, solid, aqueous solution, or gas, and under what conditions?

2. Physical characteristics. Is it vaporizable? What is its vapor pressure, boiling point, etc.?

3. Explosive limits, both upper and lower, in per cent by volume in air.

4. Flashpoint (closed cup, open cup, or both).

5. Chemical reactivity (acid, alkaline, or oxidizing).

6. Is product shock sensitive (detonable)?

7. What conditions or chemical contaminants can cause product to become dangerous?

8. Ignition temperature.

One of the foremost guides to the physical properties of flammable substances in their relation to fire hazards is the tabulation of known properties of several hundred products (NFPA 325, 1951 Edition, of the National Fire Protection Association [1]). The NFPA has granted the MCA permission to reproduce the following information.

FIRE-HAZARD PROPERTIES OF FLAMMABLE LIQUIDS, GASES AND VOLATILE SOLIDS

This tabulation of the available data on the properties of the flammable liquids and other materials listed is sponsored by the NFPA Committee on Flammable Liquids. The first edition was presented to NFPA in 1930. Successively revised and enlarged editions were published in 1935, 1941, 1945, and 1947 with several reprints in intervening years. The present text, revised in 1951, includes extensive new material.

Readers should note that this material is not an official standard of the NFPA; it is only a compilation of data from various sources presented for information.

The following table presents a summary of the available data on the tabulated properties of the various substances with indication (in the columns designated "Ref.") of the source of the information. The figures in the first line (in bold face type) applying to each substance listed are the representative values deemed suitable for general use. A selection is necessary owing to the fact that the available figures vary over a wide range, but no implication of incompetency on the part of those not quoted is intended. Minor differences are to be expected even among the most competent observers, owing to unavoidable experimental errors. The purity of the samples tested may be responsible for considerable differences in results. In the case of some of the older sources of data, information is lacking both as to the character of the samples and the details of the testing procedures.

In most cases minor variations in flash point, ignition tempera-

[1] The National Fire Protection Association was organized in 1896 to promote the science and improve the methods of fire protection and prevention, to obtain and circulate information on these subjects and to secure the cooperation of the public in establishing proper safeguards against loss of life and property by fire.

ture and explosive range have little practical significance. In case of difference of opinion as to the actual flash point or other characteristics of any specific liquid under consideration, tests should be made by some recognized testing laboratory from a sample of the particular liquid or material in question.

Flash Point of the liquid is the temperature at which it gives off vapor sufficient to form an ignitible mixture with the air near the surface of the liquid or within the vessel used. By "ignitible mixture" is meant a mixture within the explosive range (between upper and lower limits) that is capable of the propagation of flame[2] away from the source of ignition when ignited. Some evaporation takes place below the above temperature, i.e., below the flash point, when vapor does not go off freely enough to meet flash point classification requirements. This term applies mostly to flammable liquids, although there are certain solids, such as camphor and naphthalene, that slowly evaporate or volatilize at ordinary room temperature and therefore have flash points while still in the solid state.

The flash point figures represent closed cup tests except where the open cup flash point is designated by the initials "oc" following the figure. Open cup flash points, determined in a different type of testing apparatus, are usually somewhat higher than the closed cup flash point figures for the same substances. Closed cup flash point figures are commonly used in determining the classification of liquids which flash in the ordinary temperature range, but for certain materials which have relatively high flash points, the open cup flash point testing is often preferred. In the case of some of the older figures quoted in the table, there are no data to indicate whether the figures are closed or open cup tests.

Ignition Temperature of a substance, whether solid,[3] liquid or gaseous, is the minimum temperature required to initiate or

---

[2] By "propagation of flame" is here meant the spread of flame from layer to layer independently of the source of ignition. A gas or vapor mixed with air in proportions below the lower limit of flammability may burn at the source of ignition, that is, in the zone immediately surrounding the source of ignition, without propagating (spreading) away from the source of ignition.

[3] Ignition temperature of a solid is influenced by its physical condition and the rate of heating.

cause self-sustained combustion independently of the heating or heated element.

The figures on ignition temperature may vary, depending upon the test method, as the ignition temperature varies with the size, shape and material of the testing container and other factors.

Explosive or Flammable Limits. In the case of most flammable liquids and numerous flammable gases and solids, there is a minimum concentration of vapor in air or oxygen below which propagation of flame does not occur on contact with a source of ignition. There is also a maximum proportion of vapor or gas in air above which propagation of flame does not occur. These limit mixtures of vapor or gas with air, which if ignited will just propagate flame, are known as the "lower and higher explosive or flammable limits," and are usually expressed in terms of percentage by volume of gas or vapor in air.

In popular terms, a mixture below the lower explosive limits is too "lean" to explode, and a mixture above the upper explosive limits too "rich" to explode.

The explosive limit figures given in this table are based upon normal atmospheric temperatures and pressures unless otherwise indicated. There may be considerable variation in explosive limits at pressures or temperatures above or below normal.

Explosive Range. The difference between the lower and higher explosive or flammable limits, expressed in terms of percentage of vapor or gas in air by volume, is known as the "explosive range," also often referred to as the "flammable range." For example, the lower limit of flammability of gasoline at ordinary ambient temperatures is approximately 1.3 per cent vapor in air by volume, while the upper limit of flammability is about 6. By difference, the explosive or flammable range of gasoline is therefore 4.7. No attempt is made to differentiate between the terms "flammable" and "explosive" as applied to the lower and upper limits of flammability. In the case of most vapors and gases there is no basis for sharp distinctions between "flammable limits" and "explosive limits."

Vapor Density is the relative density of the vapor as compared with air, a figure less than 1 (one) indicating a vapor lighter than air, and a figure greater than 1 (one) a vapor heavier than air. The vapor density figures in the tabulation have been calculated.

Underwriters' Laboratories Classification is a standard classification for grading the relative hazard of the various flammable liquids. This classification is based upon the following scale:

Ether Class 100
Gasoline Class 90-100
Alcohol (ethyl) Class 60-70
Kerosene Class[4] 30-40
Paraffin Oil Class 10-20

Extinguishing Agents. The last column designated as "Ext. Agt." indicates extinguishing agents considered by the Factory Mutual Engineering Division as suitable for use on fires in the various materials listed. This information should be applied with caution as there are factors to be considered in any individual problem of extinguishment which cannot be covered within the limits of this tabulation. The amount and rate and method of application of the extinguishing material in relation to the size and type of fire anticipated must be carefully considered and may call for special engineering judgment, particularly in large-scale applications.

The use of standard approved equipment is also of major importance. Further details on various types of extinguishing equipment will be found in NFPA Standards on First Aid Fire Appliances, Foam Extinguishing Systems, Carbon Dioxide Extinguishing Systems, Water Spray Systems[5] and Inert Gas Systems for Fire and Explosion prevention.[6]

The code numbers (last column) indicate the following extinguishing agents:

1. Water

In the case of most flammable liquids for which water is applicable as an extinguishing agent, water from a spray or "fog" nozzle is more effective than the use of hose streams. In many

[4] A standard kerosene of 100°F. flash point (closed cup) is rated 40.
[5] National Fire Codes, Vol. IV, published by NFPA.
[6] National Fire Codes, Vol. II, published by NFPA.

cases, however, water from automatic sprinklers will control such fires. If water in any form is applied to a body of flammable liquid, which is heated above 250°F., the liquid may foam over and spread the fire.

2. Foam

Portable extinguishers of the foam type are suitable for the protection of small amounts of certain flammable liquids. Where large-scale application is required, a carefully designed permanently piped foam system is indicated.

3. Carbon Dioxide, Dry Chemical and Vaporizing Liquids

Portable extinguishers of carbon dioxide, and dry chemical types, are applicable to fires involving small quantities of flammable liquids. For large-scale protection, properly designed, permanently piped carbon dioxide systems of suitable size are necessary.

Vaporizing liquid extinguishers are applicable to a limited extent on fires of the types handled satisfactorily by carbon dioxide or dry chemical extinguishers.

4. Gas Fires

Gas fires may be extinguished with carbon dioxide, dry chemical extinguishers, and in some instances with water spray. However, it may be dangerous to extinguish the flame and allow the gas to continue to flow, because an explosive mixture may be formed with air which, if ignited, may cause far greater damage than if the original fire had been allowed to burn. The best method of extinguishing gas fires is to stop the flow of gas. Extinguishing the flame by carbon dioxide or dry chemical may be desirable where necessary to permit immediate access to valves to shut off the supply. In many cases, however, it is best to allow the flame to continue, keeping the surroundings cool with water spray to prevent ignition of other combustible materials.

Table of Common Hazardous Chemicals. In various parts of this tabulation references will be found to the Table of Common Hazardous Chemicals, available in pamphlet form from the NFPA.

Oxygen—Mixtures. The values in this table, except where otherwise indicated, are based upon experiments in normal air. In oxygen the values may be different and an increase in hazard is probable. Mixtures of two or more flammable materials may have properties different from their components. In the case of mixtures it is common practice to base precautions on the properties of the more hazardous components.

Abbreviations. The abbreviations used in this table are in accordance with common practice. Those most frequently used are:

o—ortho	iso—isometric
m—meta	prim— primary
n—normal	sec—secondary
p—para	sym—symmetrical
>—greater than	ter—tertiary
<—less than	

	FLASH POINT Deg. F.	Ref.	IGNITION TEMP. Deg. F.	Ref.	EXPLOSIVE LIMITS Per Cent by Volume Lower	Upper	Ref.	Sp. Gr. (Water = 1)	Vapor Density Air = 1	Boiling Point Deg. F.	Und. Lab. Class	Ext. Agt.
Acetal $CH_3CH(OC_2H_5)_2$	—5	26	446	48	1.65		48	0.821	4.08	215		3
Acetaldehyde CH_3CHO	—36	26	365	26;31	4	57	5;26	0.783	1.52	70		1,3
Acetanalide $CH_3CONHC_6H_5$ (Antifebrin)	(o.c.)345	26	1015 1015 1017	26 17				1.21	4.65	581		1,3
Acetic Acid (Glacial) CH_3COOH	104 111 107 104	6;9;10 28 26	800 800-925 1050	28 26	4.0		5;26	1.05	2.07	245		1,3
			Note: See also Table of Common Hazardous Chemicals.									
Acetic Acid	115 111	7;18 13	Note: Ordinary acetic acid is the same as glacial acetic acid with water. The properties of ordinary acetic acid depend upon the strength of the solution. In concentrated form its properties approach those of glacial acetic acid. In dilute solution it is non-hazardous.									
Acetic Anhydride $(CH_3CO)_2O$ (Acetyl Oxide)	121 127 110 121	28 10 9;26	600 600-675 752	28 26	2.67	10.13	36					1,3
Acetone CH_3COCH_3 (Dimethyl Ketone)	0 3F —4 3 0-36 34 0 (o.c.)15	2;10;18 22 28;43 1 J 15;26 26	1000 1000-1050 1000 1055	28 26 48	2.55 3 2.15 2.55 2.40 @ 212°	12.8 11.0 13.0 12.8	5 28 16;35 50	0.792	2.00	134	90	3
					Note: See also Table of Common Hazardous Chemicals.							
Acetone Cyanohydrin $(CH_3)_2C(OH)CN$			1270	17				0.932	2.93	248 Decom- poses		3
Acetonyl Acetone $CH_2COCH_3)_2$ (1,2—Diacetylethane)	174 174 (o.c.)180	26;83 26;83	920	26				0.973	3.94	378		1,3
Acetophenone $C_6H_5COCH_3$	221	26						1.03	4.14	396		1,2,3
Acetotoluide —p $CH_3C_6H_4NHCOCH_3$	335	26						1.212	5.14	584		1,2,3
Acetyl Acetone $CH_2(COCH_3)_2$ (2,4—Pentanedione)	93 93 (o.c.)105	26;83 26						0.975	3.45	285		1,3
Acetyl Chloride CH_3COCl	40 40 75	18;26 42						1.105	2.70	124		1,3
Acetylene C_2H_2	Gas		635	26	2.5 2.6 3.0 2.5	80 82 80	1 5 26		0.91	—119		4
Acetyl Peroxide $(CH_3CO)_2O_2$	(o.c.)113	26;85						1.18				1,3
Acrolein $CH_2:CHCHO$ (Acrylic Aldehyde)	<0	51	532 532 Unstable	52 26				0.84	1.94	125		4
Acrylonitrile $CH_2:CHCN$ (Vinyl Cyanide)	(o.c.)32	70	898	48	3.05	17.0	48;90	0.800	1.83	171		3

	FLASH POINT		IGNITION TEMP.		EXPLOSIVE LIMITS Per Cent by Volume			Sp. Gr. (Water =1)	Vapor Den-sity Air=1	Boiling Point	Und. Lab.	Ext.
	Deg. F.	Ref.	Deg. F.	Ref.	Low-er	Up-per	Ref.			Deg. F.	Class	Agt.
Adipic Acid $COOH(CH_2)_4COOH$ (Dicyclohexyl)	385	13;26							5.04	700		1,2,3
Alcohol	See Ethyl Alcohol, Methyl Alcohol, etc.											
Aldol $CH_3CH(OH)CH_2CHO$ (Oxybutyric Aldehyde)	181	26	530 530 478	26 17				1.11	3.04	380		1,3
Allyl Alcohol $CH_2:CHCH_2OH$	70 70 (o.c.)75	9;10;26 26	713	26	3.0	18.0	26;71	0.854	2.00	206		3
Allyl Amine $CH_2:CHCH_2NH_2$			705	17				0.761	2.0	128		
Allyl Bromide $CH_2:CHCH_2Br$			563	17				1.398	4.17	160		
Allyl Chlorformate $CH_2:CHCH_2OCOCl$ (Allyl Chlorcarbonate)	88	42						1.14	4.2	223-237		3
Allyl Chloride $CH_2:CHCH_2Cl$	—25	75	737 909 737	52 26	3.28	11.15	26	0.937	2.64	113		3,4
Allylene $CH_3C:CH$	Gas				1.74		26		1.38	—18		4
2-Amino-1-Butanol $CH_3CH_2CHNH_2$-CH_2OH	(o.c.)165	26						0.944	3.07	352		1,3
Aminoethylethanolamine $NH_2C_2H_4NHC_2H_4OH$	(o.c.)275	26;83	695	26				1.030	3.59	469.4		1,3
Aminoethyl Morpholine $C_2H_4OC_2H_4NC_2H_4NH_2$								1.000	4.49	395.6		1,3
2-Amino-2-Methyl-1-Propanol $(CH_3)_2C(NH_2)CH_2OH$	(o.c.)159	53						0.934	3.04	329		3
Ammonia (Anhydrous) NH_3	Gas		1204 1204	26;39	16 16.0	25 25	5;26;28		0.587	—37		4
								Note: Non-flammable in air except in comparatively high concentrations. See Table of Common Hazardous Chemicals.				
Amyl Acetate (Pure) $CH_3COOC_5H_{11}$	77 77 76 (o.c.)80	28 26 26	750 714 815 750-800 750	11;26 21 28 52	1.10		73	0.879	4.49	300	55-60	3
Comm.	70 70	18										
Amyl Acetate—iso $CH_3COOCH_2CH_2$-$CH(CH_3)_2$ (Banana Oil)	77 77 (o.c.)100	10;13;26 26	715 714 715 729	25;52 26 50	1.0 @212°		50	0.876	4.49	290	55-60	3
Amyl Acetate—sec $CH_3COOCH(CH_3)$-$(CH_2)_2CH_3$	89 89 (o.c.)111	26 25						0.862	4.48	249		3
Amyl Alcohol—n $CH_3(CH_2)_3CH_2OH$ (Primary Amyl Alcohol) (Fusel Oil)	100 108 100-110 100 91 (o.c.)120	22 18 28 26 26	700 673 660 700-725 621	25 11 28 26	1.2		5;26	0.817	3.04	280	40	3

	FLASH POINT		IGNITION TEMP.		EXPLOSIVE LIMITS Per Cent by Volume			Sp. Gr. (Water = 1)	Vapor Density Air = 1	Boiling Point Deg. F.	Und. Lab. Class	Ext. Agt.
	Deg. F.	Ref.	Deg. F.	Ref.	Low-er	Up-per	Ref.					
Amyl Alcohol—prim. iso (CH₃)₂CHCH₂- CH₂OH (Butyl Carbinol—iso)	109 114 109	28 26	650 650-725 667	28 26	1.2		84	0.813	3.04	270	35-40	3
Amyl Alcohol—sec. n CH₃CH₂CH₂CH- (OH)CH₃	94 (o.c.)102	26;28 26	650 650-725	26;28				0.810	3.04	245	40-45	2
Amyl Alcohol—sec. iso (CH₃)₂CHCH- (OH)CH₃	103	26						0.819	3.04	235		3
Amyl Alcohol—ter. CH₃CH₂(CH₃)₂COH (Dimethyl Ethyl Carbinol)	67 68 67 70 (o.c.)75	13 26 94 26	819	17				0.81	3.03	215		3
Amylamine C₅H₁₁NH₂	(o.c.)45	26;87						0.776	3.01	219.2		3
Amyl Benzene C₆H₅C₅H₁₁	(o.c.)150	26;87						0.78-0.85	5.11	365		1,2,3
Amyl Chloride—n CH₃(CH₂)₃CH₂Cl	(o.c.)55	26	498	52	1.4		26	0.878	3.67	223		2,3
Amyl Chloride—ter. CH₃CH₂CCl(CH₃)- CH₃			649	17				1.407	3.67	107		2,3
Amyl Chlorides (Mixed) C₅H₁₁Cl	(o.c.)38	26						0.88	3.67	186-228		2,3
Amylene—n CH₃(CH₂)₂CH:CH₂	(o.c.)0	26	523	52	1.6	7.7	5:26	0.666	2.42	98		2,3
Amyl Ether C₅H₁₁OC₅H₁₁ (Diamyl Ether)	(o.c.)135	26;87						0.78-0.80	5.46	338		1,2,3
Amyl Mercaptans (Mixed) C₅H₁₁SH	(o.c.)65	26;87						0.825	3.59	176-257		1,3
Amyl Methyl Alcohol CH₃(CH₂)₂CH(CH₃)- CH₂OH	114	12;26						0.804	3.52	266		3
Amyl Methyl Ketone CH₃CO(CH₂)₄CH₃	(o.c.)120	26;83	991	52				0.817	3.94	301		3,6
Amyl Naphthalene C₁₀H₇C₅H₁₁	(o.c.)225	26						0.973	6.86	550		2,3
Amyl Phenol-o C₅H₁₁C₆H₄OH	(o.c.)219	26;87						0.96-0.97	5.66	649		1,2,3
Amyl Propionate C₂H₅COO(CH₂)₄CH₃	(o.c.)106	26						0.869-0.873	5.00	275-347		1,3
Amyl Salicylate HOC₆H₄COOC₅H₁₁	270	13;26						1.065	7.17	512.		1,2,3
Amyl Stearate CH₃(CH₂)₁₆COO- C₅H₁₁	(o.c.)365	26						0.86		680		1,2,3
Amyl Sulfides (Mixed) C₅H₁₁S	(o.c.)185	26						0.85-0.91		338-356		2,3
Amyl Toluene C₅H₁₁C₆H₄CH₃	(o.c.)180	26						0.87		400-415		2,3
Amyl Xylol Ether C₅H₁₁OC₆H₃(CH₃)₂	(o.c.)205	26						0.907		480-500		1,2,3

	FLASH POINT Deg. F.	Ref.	IGNITION TEMP. Deg. F.	Ref.	EXPLOSIVE LIMITS Per Cent by Volume Lower	Upper	Ref.	Sp. Gr. (Water =1)	Vapor Density Air=1	Boiling Point Deg. F.	Und. Lab. Class	Ext. Agt.
Aniline C₆H₅NH₂ (Aniline Oil) (Amino Benzene)	168 168 183 156	26 28 13	1000 1418 1000-1025 1143	26;31 28 17				1.022	3.22	363	20-25	2,3
Aniline Hydrochloride C₆H₅NH₂·HCl	(o.c.)380	26						1.22	4.46	473		1,3
Anthracene C₆H₄(CH)₂C₆H₄ (Green Oil)	250	26	881	26;52	0.63		26	1.25	6.15	644		1,2,3
Anthraquinone C₆H₄(CO)₂C₆H₄	365	26						1.438	7.16	716		1,2,3
Asphalt (Typical) (Petroleum Pitch)	400+	26	905	26				0.95-1.1		>700		1,2,3
Benzaldehyde C₆H₅CHO (Artificial Almond Oil)	148 147-148 148	28 26	377 356 377	31 28				1.05	3.66	355		1,2,3
Benzedrine C₆H₅CH₂CH(CH₃)NH₂ (Amphetamine)	>80	26						0.931		392		1,3
Benzene	See Benzol											
Benzine	0 or less 5 0 or less 52 24	10 2 122 122			1.1 2.6 1.1	4.8 4.8	8 5		4.48				2,3

Note: Benzine is an indefinite term. It roughly corresponds to a volatile gasoline.

	FLASH POINT Deg. F.	Ref.	IGNITION TEMP. Deg. F.	Ref.	EXPLOSIVE LIMITS Per Cent by Volume Lower	Upper	Ref.	Sp. Gr. (Water =1)	Vapor Density Air=1	Boiling Point Deg. F.	Und. Lab. Class	Ext. Agt.
Benzoic Acid C₆H₅COOH	250 250-268 250	1;13 26	1065	74				1.266	4.21	482		1,3
Benzol (Benzene) C₆H₆	12 —4 10-16 12	28 13 26;88	1000 1076-1079 1076 1060 1000	25 11;26 50 88	1.5 1.4 1.5 1.4 1.4 1.10 @212°	8.0 8.0 8.0 5.5 7.0	26 11;28;88 31 5 50	0.88	2.77	176	95-100	2,3
Benzotrifluoride C₆H₅CF₃	54	54						1.197	5.0	216		2,3
Benzoyl Chloride C₆H₅COCl	162 215 162	26 42						1.212	4.88	387		1,2,3
Benzoyl Peroxide (C₆H₅CO)₂O₂ (Lucidol, White Granular)			Decomposes @250°	26				Note: See also Table of Common Hazardous Chemicals. Explodes				1,2,3
Benzyl Acetate CH₃COOCH₂C₆H₅	216	13;26	862	26				1.06	5.17	417		1,2,3
Benzyl Alcohol C₆H₅CH₂OH (Phenyl Carbinol)	213 212 213	13 26	817	11;26				1.04	3.72	403		1,2,3
Benzyl Benzoate C₆H₅COOCH₂C₆H₅	298	13;26						1.114	7.31	614		1,2,3

	FLASH POINT Deg. F.	Ref.	IGNITION TEMP. Deg. F.	Ref.	EXPLOSIVE LIMITS Per Cent by Volume Low-er	Up-per	Ref.	Sp. Gr. (Water =1)	Vapor Den-sity Air=1	Boiling Point Deg. F.	Und. Lab. Class	Ext. Agt.
Benzyl Cellosolve C6H5CH2OCH2-CH2OH	(o.c.)265	26	665	26				1.07		493		1,3
Benzyl Chloride C6H5CH2Cl	153	26	1161	52	1.1		44	1.103	4.36	349		1,2,3
Benzyl Diethylamine C6H5CH2N(C2H5)2	(o.c.)170	26						0.89		405-420		1,2,3
Blast-furnace Gas	See Gas											
Borneol C10H17OH (Borneo Camphor)	150	26						1.01	5.31	413 Sublimes		1,3
					Note: See Table of Common Hazardous Chemicals.							
Brandy (See Also Ethyl Alcohol and Water)	84	40										3
Bromobenzene C6H5Br (Phenyl Bromide)	149 149	1;13;26						1.497	5.41	313		1,2,3
Bronzing Liquid May be below 80		2										2,3
Butadiene—1,3 CH2:CHCH:CH2	Gas		842	92	2.0	11.5	49	0.621	1.87	24		4
Butadiene Monoxide CH2:CHCHOCH2 (Vinylethylene Oxide)	<—58	26						0.869	2.41	151		3,4
Butane—n C4H10	—76	26	806 805 806 761	17:26 27 17	1.6 1.9 1.6	6.5 8.5 6.5	5;12 26;27	0.599	2.046	33		4
					Note: See Table of Common Hazardous Chemicals.							
Butane—iso (CH3)3CH (2—Methyl Propane)	Gas		1010 1010 864	26 17	1.9	8.5	12	0.58	2.01	14		4
Butanol (See Butyl Alcohol)												
Butene—1 CH3CH2CH:CH2 (a—Butylene)	—112	26;89	723	17	1.7	9.0	1;5;- 12;26	0.601	1.939	23		4
Butene—2 CH3CH:CHCH3 (β—Butylene)			615	17				0.635	1.939	34		4
Butylacetanilide—n CH3(CH2)3N(C6H5)-COCH3	206	55						0.992	6.6	531-538		1,3
Butyl Acetate—n CH3COOC4H9 C.P	72 75-80 82 72 (o.c.90) 84	14 15 26 26 28	790 792-841 790 700-825 791	14 26 28 11	1.7 1.7 1.7	15 15	5 26	0.88	4.00	260	50-60	3
Butyl Acetate—iso CH3COOCH2-CH(CH3)2	64	13;26						0.871	4.00	244		3

	FLASH POINT		IGNITION TEMP.		EXPLOSIVE LIMITS Per Cent by Volume			Sp. Gr. (Water =1)	Vapor Density Air=1	Boiling Point Deg. F.	Und. Lab. Class	Ext. Agt.
	Deg. F.	Ref.	Deg. F.	Ref.	Lower	Upper	Ref.					
Butyl Acetate—sec. $CH_3COOCH(CH_3)$-C_2H_5	(o.c.)88	26			1.7		26	0.858	4.00	221		3
Butyl Acetyl Ricinoleate $C_{17}H_{32}(OCOCH_3)$-$(COOC_4H_9)$	230	15	725	84				0.940		428		1,2,3
Butyl Alcohol—n $CH_3(CH_2)_2CH_2OH$ (Butanol—1) (Primary Butyl Alcohol) "	84 / 95 / 84 / 100 / (o.c.)110	15;43 / 26 / 13;28 / 26	650 / 692 / 693 / 650-725 / 689	25 / 26 / 28 / 50	1.7 / 1.7 / 1.56 / @212°	18 / / / / 18	26 / / 50 / 103	0.806	2.55	243	40	1,3
Butyl Alcohol—iso $(CH_3)_2CHCH_2OH$	82 / 82 / 88 / (o.c.)105	10;26;13 / 28 / 26	800 / 777 / 700-800 / 825	48 / 28 / 26	1.68		5;26	0.805	2.55	225	40-45	1,3
Butyl Alcohol—sec. $CH_3CH_2CHOHCH_3$ (Butanol—2)	75	26;86	777	52				0.808-0.812	2.55	201		1,3
Butyl Alcohol—ter. $(CH_3)_2COHCH_3$	52	9;10;26	892 / 901 / 892	26 / 48	2.35	8.0	48	0.786	2.55	181		1,3
Butylamine—n $C_4H_9NH_2$	45 / 45 / <40	83 / 26	594	17				0.74-0.76	2.52	172		3
Butylamine—iso $(CH_3)_2CHCH_2NH_2$	15	14	705	17				0.733	2.52	150		3
Butylamine Oleate $C_{17}H_{33}COONH_3C_4H_9$	(o.c.)150	26;94						0.891				3
Butyl Benzene—n $C_6H_5C_4H_9$			774	17				0.862	4.62	356		2,3
Butyl Benzene—iso $(CH_3)_2CHCH_2C_6H_5$			802	17				0.867	4.62	341		2,3
Butyl Benzene—sec. $C_6H_5CH(CH_3)C_2H_5$	126	1;13;26	829	17				0.86	4.62	345		2,3
Butyl Benzene—ter. $C_6H_5C(CH_3)_3$			838	17				0.871	4.62	337		2,3
Butyl Benzyl Phthalate $C_4H_9COOC_6H_4$-$COOCH_2C_6H_5$	390	56						1.116	10.8	698		2,3
Butyl Bromide—n $CH_3(CH_2)_2CH_2Br$ (Bromo Butane—1)	(o.c.)55	26	600	26				1.272	4.72	215		3
Butyl Butyrate $CH_3(CH_2)_2COOC_4H_9$	(o.c.)128	26						0.874		305		1,2,3
Butyl Carbinol—iso	See Amy Alcohol—prim. iso											
Butyl Carbinol—ter. $(CH_3)_3CCH_2OH$	98	7							3.03			3
Butyl Carbitol $C_4H_9OCH_2CH_2$-OCH_2CH_2OH	172	26	442	26				0.955	5.58	448		1,3
Butyl Carbitol Acetate $C_4H_9OCH_2CH_2$-$OCH_2CH_2OOCCH_3$	(o.c.)240	26;66	570	26				0.987		474		1,2,3

	FLASH POINT Deg. F.	Ref.	IGNITION TEMP. Deg. F.	Ref.	EXPLOSIVE LIMITS Per Cent by Volume Low-er	Up-per	Ref.	Sp. Gr. (Water =1)	Vapor Density Air=1	Boiling Point Deg. F.	Und. Lab. Class	Ext. Agt.
Butyl Cellosolve $CH_2OHCH_2OC_4H_9$	141 141 140	26 19	472	26				0.902	4.07	340		1,2
Butyl Cellosolve Acetate $C_4H_9O(CH_2)_2$-$OOCCH_3$	(o.c.)180	26						0.943		370		1,2,3
Butyl Chloride—n C_4H_9Cl	(o.c.)20	26	860	73	1.85	10.1	73	0.887	3.20	170		2,3
Butyl Decalin $C_4H_9C_{10}H_{17}$	500	60										1,3
Butyl Decalin—ter. $C_4H_9C_{10}H_{17}$	640	64										1,3
Butyl Diethanolamine—n $C_4H_9N(C_2H_4OH)_2$	(o.c.)245	26;87						0.97	5.55	5.04		1,2,3
α—Butylene	See Butene—1											
β—Butylene	See Butene—2											
γ—Butylene (Butylene—iso)	See 2—Methyl Propene											
Butylene Chloride C_4H_7Cl					2.25	9.25	71	0.926	3.13	162		2,3
β— Butylene Glycol $CH_3CH(OH)CH_2$-CH_2OH	228	26	710	26				1.006	3.10	405		1,3
Butyl Ethanolamine—n $CH_2(CH_2)_3NHCH_2$-CH_2OH	(o.c.)170	26						0.89	4.03	311		1,2,3
Butyl Ether—n	See Dibutyl Ether											
Butyl Formate—n $HCOOC_4H_9$	64	1:13:26	612	52				0.911	3.52	225		2,3
Butyl Hydroperoxide —ter. $(CH_3)_3COOH$	55 55 (o.c.)65	26;91 26;91						0.860	2.07			3
Butyl Lactate $CH_3CH(OH)$-$COOC_4H_9$	(o.c.)160	15 26	720	26				0.968	5.04	320		2,3
Butyl Methyl Ketone $CH_3CO(CH_2)_3CH_3$	(o.c.)95	26			1.22	8.0	26	0.830	3.45	262		2,3
iso—Butyl Methyl Ketone $CH_3COCH_2CH(CH_3)_2$ (Hexone)	73 73 74 (o.c.)75	26 12 26;83	858		1.34 17 @ 122°	8.00 @ 212°	114	0.803	3.45	244		2,3
Butyl Monoethanolamine —n $C_4H_9NHC_2H_4OH$	(o.c.)170	26;87						0.89	4.03	378		1,2,3
Butyl Naphthalene $C_4H_9C_{10}H_7$	680	60										1,3
Buytl Oleate $C_{17}H_{33}COOC_4H_9$	(o.c.)356	26						0.873		343		1,2,3
Butyl Oxalate $(COOC_4H_9)_2$ (Butyl Ethanedioate)	(o.c.)265	26;43						0.989- 0.993				1,2,3
Butyl Perbenzoate—ter. $C_6H_5COOOC(CH_3)_3$	66 66 (o.c.)75	26;91 26;91						1.035	6.69	235 Decom- poses		3

	FLASH POINT Deg. F.	Ref.	IGNITION TEMP. Deg. F.	Ref.	EXPLOSIVE LIMITS Per Cent by Volume Lower	Upper	Ref.	Sp. Gr. (Water =1)	Vapor Density Air=1	Boiling Point Deg. F.	Und. Lab. Class	Ext. Agt.
Butyl Phthallyl Butyl Glycollate $C_6H_4(COO)_2(C_4H_9)\cdot CH_2COOC_4H_9$	(o.c.)390	26						1.097	11.6	653		1,2,3
Butyl Propionate—n $C_2H_5CO_2C_4H_9$	90 105 90	10 26	800 802 800	11 26				0.875	4.49	295		2,3
Butyl Ricinoleate $C_{18}H_{33}O_3C_4H_9$	230	26						0.906		790		1,2,3
Butyl Stearate—n $C_{17}H_{35}COOC_4H_9$	320	26						0.855		650		1,2,3
Butyl Tetralin—ter. $C_4H_9C_{10}H_{11}$	680	64										1,3
Butyl Trichlorosilane $CH_3(CH_2)_3SiCl_3$	(o.c.)130	57						1.161	6.5	300		2,3
Butyraldehyde $CH_3(CH_2)_2CHO$	20 64 20	15 26	446	52				0.817	2.48	169		3
Butyraldehyde—iso $(CH_3)_2CHCHO$ (2—Methyl Propanal)	—40	26	490	26				0.813	2.49	142		3
Butyraldoxime C_4H_8NOH (Butanal Oxime)	136	75						0.923	3.01	306		2,3
Butyric Acid—n $CH_3(CH_2)_2COOH$	170	12;26	1026	52				0.960	3.04	327		1,3
Butyric Anhydride—n $[CH_3(CH_2)_2CO]_2O$	190	12;26						0.978	5.38	388		1,3
Butyrone $(C_3H_7)_2CO$ (4—Heptanone)	120	12;26						0.815	3.93	290		3
Camphor $C_9H_{16}CO$ (Gum Camphor)	150 150 180	26 16	871	26	Note: See Table of Common Hazardous Chemicals.			0.999	5.24	408		2,3
Camphor Oil (light) (Liquid Camphor)	117 117 131	26 10						0.88		347-392		2,3
Caproic Acid—n $(CH_3)(CH_2)_4COOH$ (Hexanoic Acid) (Hexoic Acid—n)	(o.c.)215	26;83						0.929	4.01	400		1,2,3
Caprylyl Chloride $CH_3(CH_2)_6COCl$	180	42						0.958	5.6	384		2,3
Carbitol $CH_2OHCH_2OCH_2\text{-}CH_2OC_2H_5$	201 210 201	12 26						0.99	4.62	396		1,3
Carbitol Acetate $C_2H_5O(CH_2)_2O\text{-}(CH_2)_2CO_2CH_3$	225 225 (o.c.)230	12;26 66						1.013	6.07	424		1,3
Carbitol Phthalate $C_6H_4(COOC_2H_4\text{-}OC_2H_4OC_2H_5)_2$ (Dicarbitol Phthalate)	405 405 (o.c.)475	26 26						1.121		>500		1,2,3

	FLASH POINT		IGNITION TEMP.		EXPLOSIVE LIMITS Per Cent by Volume			Sp. Gr. (Water = 1)	Vapor Density Air = 1	Boiling Point Deg. F.	Und. Lab. Class	Ext. Agt.
	Deg. F.	Ref.	Deg. F.	Ref.	Lower	Upper	Ref.					
Carbon Disulfide CS₂ (Carbon Bisulfide)	—22 4 —22 —15	10 22;26;28 13	212 212-223 261 257 212-338	28 25 26 6	1.0 1.0 4.1	50 50	5; 26;28 8	1.3	2.64	114	110+	1,3
							Note: See Table of Common Hazardous Chemicals.					
Carbon Monoxide CO	Gas		1204 1191-1216 1193-1211 1204	31 30 26	12.5 12.5 16.3 12.5	74 74 71.2 74.2	5;28 31 26		0.967	—314		4
Carbon Oxysulfide COS (Carbonyl Sulfide)	Gas				11.9	28.5	5;26	1.24	2.10			4
Carbon Remover, Liquid	<80	2										3
Carnauba Wax (Brazil Wax)	540	26						Note: Melting point 185°.				1,3
Castor Oil (Ricinus Oil)	445 445 487	26 9	840 617 840	1 26				0.96		595		1,2,3
Castor Oil (Hydrogenated) (C₁₈H₃₅O₃)₃C₃H₅	401	42										2,3
Cationic Amine—220 C₁₇H₃₃CN(CH₃)₂- NCH₂CH₂OH	(o.c.)465	26										1,2,3
Cellosolve C₂H₅O(CH₂)₄OH (Ethyl Cellosolve)	104 111 104	12 26	460	26	2.6	15.7	26	0.931	3.10	275		3
Cellosolve Acetate CH₃COOCH₂:CH₂- OC₂H₅	124 127 174 (o.c.)150	19 26 66	715	26	1.71		26	0.975	4.72	313		3
Chlorobenzene C₆H₅Cl (Phenyl Chloride)	85 90 84 91 85	26 13 10 16	1100- 1200 1100- 1200 >1245	58 26	1.8 (@ 212°	9.6 @ 302°)	46	1.11	3.88	270	40-50	2,3
Chlorobenzotrifluoride—n ClC₆H₄CF₃	138	59						1.379	6.24	306		2,3
Chloroethyl Acetate C₂H₄ClOOCCH₃ (Ethyl Chloroacetate)	129 153 129	13 1;26						1.178	4.21	293		1,2,3
2—Chloro—5—Nitro— Benzotrifluoride C₆H₃CF₃(2—Cl, 5- —NO₂)	275	61						1.55	7.8	446		2,3
Chloronitroethane—1,1 C₂H₄NO₂Cl	133	76						1.258	3.77	344*		1,3
Chloronitropropane—1,1 CHNO₂ClC₂H₅	144	76						1.209	4.26	285*		1,3
Chloronitropropane—2,2 CH₃CNO₂ClCH₃	135	76							4.26	273*		1,3

*Explodes upon Rapid Heating. Ref. 26;77.

	FLASH POINT Deg. F.	Ref.	IGNITION TEMP. Deg. F.	Ref.	EXPLOSIVE LIMITS Per Cent by Volume Lower	Upper	Ref.	Sp. Gr. (Water =1)	Vapor Density Air=1	Boiling Point Deg. F.	Und. Lab. Class	Ext. Agt.
Cleaning Fluid	<80	2										3
Cleaning Solvents of Kerosene Class, such as Stoddard Solvent, Varnolene, Varsol, etc.	100-110 100-110 or higher	26 38	450 493 495 450-500	25 21 26	1.1	6.0	26	Note: Underwriters' Laboratories, Inc., List of Gas, Oil and Miscellaneous Appliances gives the flash points of cleaning solvents sold under various trade names.			30-40	
Coal Gas	See Gas											4
Coal Tar Light Oil	<80	2							<1			2,3
Coal Tar Pitch	405	26										1,2,3
Cocoanut Oil Refined Crude	420 548 420	24 24;26							0.91			1,2,3
Collodion $C_{12}H_{16}O_6(NO_3)_4$- $C_{12}H_{17}O_7(NO_3)_3$ (Solution of Nitrated Cellulose in Ether-Alcohol.)	<0 0 or less <0	2;18 26										3
Cologne Spirits	See Ethyl Alcohol											3
Columbian Spirits	See Methyl Alcohol											3
Corn Oil	490 480 490 (o.c.)610	3 26 84	740	26				0.92				1,2,3
Cooking (Mazola)								<1				3
Cottonseed Oil (Refined)	486 476 486 (o.c.)610	9 26;28 84	650 650-800 650	28 26				0.925				1,2,3
Cooking (Wesson)								<1				3
Creosote Oil	165	26	637	26				>1		382-752		1,2,3
Cresol—o $CH_3C_6H_4OH$	178 177 178	13 26	1110 1110 1038	52 26	1.35 @ 300°		26	1.05	3.72	376		1,2,3
Cresol—m or p $CH_3C_6H_4OH$	187	1;13;26	1159 1159 1038	52 50	1.06 @ 302°		50	1.04	3.72	395		1,3
Cresyl Diphenyl Phosphate $(C_6H_5O)_2[(CH_3)_2$- $C_6H_4O]PO_4$	450	56						1.208	11.7	734		3
Crotonaldehyde $CH_3(CH)_2CHO$ (Butenal—2)	55 55	12;26	450	52	2.95	15.5	26	0.853	2.41	216		3
Crotonylene CH_3CCCH_3	63	78			1.37		26		1.91	83		2,3
Cumene $C_6H_5CH(CH_3)_2$ (Propyl Benzene—iso) (Cumol)	102 126 102	13 9;10						0.864	4.14	311		2,3

	FLASH POINT Deg. F.	Ref.	IGNITION TEMP. Deg. F.	Ref.	EXPLOSIVE LIMITS Per Cent by Volume Low-er	Up-per	Ref.	Sp. Gr. (Water =1)	Vapor Density Air=1	Boiling Point Deg. F.	Und. Lab. Class	Ext. Agt.
Cyanamide CNNH$_2$	285	26						1.073	1.45	500 Decomposes		1,3
Cyclobutane C$_4$H$_8$ (Tetraethylene)	<50	26						0.70	1.93	55		4
Cyclohexane C$_6$H$_{12}$ (Hexamethylene)	1 / 1 / —4	13;26 / 50	514 / 514 / 498	58 / 17	1.31 / 1.3 / 1.31 / 1.01 @212°	8.35 / 8.3 / 8.35	5 / 26 / 50	0.779	2.90	176	90-95	2,3
Cyclohexanol C$_6$H$_{11}$OH (Hexalin)	154	13;26						0.962	3.45	322		1,2,3
Cyclohexanone C$_6$H$_{10}$O	147 / 117 / 111	13;26 / 50	847	58	1.11 @212°		50	0.947	3.38	313	35-40	3
Cyclohexanone Δ C$_6$H$_8$O	93	13;26							3.31			3
Cyclohexyl Acetate CH$_3$CO$_2$C$_6$H$_{11}$ (Hexalin Acetate)	136	13;26							4.90	350		2,3
Cyclohexylamine C$_6$H$_{11}$NH$_2$	(o.c.)90	26	560	26				0.865	3.42	274		3
Cyclohexyltrichlorosilane C$_6$H$_{11}$SiCl$_3$	(o.c.)196	57						1.2	7.5	406		2,3
Cyclopropane C$_3$H$_6$	Gas		928	52	2.40 / 2.40 / 2.41	10.4 / 10.4 / 10.3	16 / 26	1.45 Note: See Table of Common Hazardous Chemicals.		—29		4
Cymene CH$_3$C$_6$H$_4$CH(CH$_3$)$_2$ (p—Cymene) Tech.	117 / 117 / 127	28 / 58	921 / 833	26 @212° / 58	0.7		26	0.86	4.62	334	30-35	2,3
Decahydronaphthalene C$_{10}$H$_{18}$ (Decalin)	136	13;26	504	76				0.893	4.76	379		2,3
Decane—n CH$_3$(CH$_2$)$_8$CH$_3$	115	26	482 / >500 / 482 / 406	26 / 52 / 17	0.67	2.6	11;26	0.730	4.90	344		2,3
Denatured Alcohol	60 / 40-60 / 55 / 61 / 60	2;10 / 3;22 / 28 / 26	750 / 750-810	28				0.82	1.60	176	70	3
Government Formula CD-5	60-62	14										
CD-5A	60-61	14										
CD-10	49-59	14										
SD-1	57	14										
SD-2B	56	14										
SD-3A	59	14										
SD-13A	<19	14										
SD-17	60	14										
SD-23A	35	14										
SD-30	59	14										
SD-39B	60	14										
SD-39C	59	14										
SD-40M	59	14										

	FLASH POINT Deg. F.	Ref.	IGNITION TEMP. Deg. F.	Ref.	EXPLOSIVE LIMITS Per Cent by Volume Low-er	Up-per	Ref.	Sp. Gr. (Water = 1)	Vapor Density Air = 1	Boiling Point Deg. F.	Und. Lab. Class	Ext. Agt.
Diacetone Alcohol CH_3COCH_2C- $(CH_3)_2OH$	48		1118					0.931	4.00	328		1,3
Acetone Free	136	26	1190	26								
Technical	40-57	15										
Commercial (Diacetone)	48	26	1118	26								
Diamylamine $(C_5H_{11})_2NH$	124 124 (o.c.)158	26 26						0.778	5.42	356		2,3
Diamylene $C_{10}H_{20}$	(o.c.)118	26;94						0.77-0.78		302		2,3
Diamyl Naphthalene $C_{10}H_6(C_5H_{11})_2$	(o.c.)315	26;94						0.93-0.94	9.26	624		2,3
Diamyl Phenol—2,4 $(C_5H_{11})_2C_6H_3OH$	(o.c.)260	26;94						0.93-0.94	8.08	527		2,3
Di-ter-amyl Phenoxy Ethanol $C_6H_3(C_5H_{11})_2-$ OC_2H_4OH	(o.c.)300	79						0.959	9.6	615		3
Diamyl Phthalate—n $C_6H_4(COOC_5H_{11})_2$	245	26						1.023		475-490 @50 m.m.		1,2,3
Diamyl Sulfide $(C_5H_{11})_2S$	(o.c.)185	26;87						0.898	6.0	338-356		1,2,3
Dianisidine $[NH_2(OCH_3)C_6H_3]_2$	403	13;26										1,3
Dibenzyl Ether $(C_6H_5CH_2)O-$ $(C_6H_5CH_2)$	275	13;26						1.036	6.82	568		1,2,3
Dibutoxy Methane $CH_2(OC_4H_9)_2$	140	26						0.838	5.5	330-370		2,3
Dibutylamine—n $(C_4H_9)_2NH$	(o.c.)135	26;94						0.76	4.46	322		2,3
Dibutylamine—iso $[(CH_3)_2CHCH_2]_2NH$	85	62						0.74	4.45	273-286		2,3
Dibutylaminoethanol—n $(C_4H_9)_2NC_2H_4OH$	(o.c.)200	26;94						0.86	5.97	432		1,3
Dibutyl Ether—n $C_4H_9OC_4H_9$	77 77 100	15;26 12	382	26				0.769	4.48	286		3
Dibutyl Ketone—iso $[(CH_3)_2CHCH_2]_2CO$ (Isovalerone)	120 120 140	63 26						0.81	4.9	335		3
Dibutyl Maleate $(—CHCO_2C_4H_9)_2$	(o.c.)285	65						0.99		Decomposes		
Dibutyl Oxalate—n $C_4H_9OOCCOOC_4H_9$	220	15;26						1.01				1,2,3
Dibutyl Phthalate—o $C_6H_4(CO_2C_4H_9)_2$	315 316-345 320 315 340	15 13 26 56	757	26				1.045	9.58	690		1,2,3

	FLASH POINT Deg. F.	Ref.	IGNITION TEMP. Deg. F.	Ref.	EXPLOSIVE LIMITS Per Cent by Volume Low-er	Up-per	Ref.	Sp. Gr. (Water =1)	Vapor Density Air=1	Boiling Point Deg. F.	Und. Lab. Class	Ext. Agt.
Dibutyl Phthalate—m $C_6H_4(CO_2C_4H_9)_2$ (Dibutyl Phthalate—iso)	322 322 328	13;26 11							9.58			1,2,3
Dibutyl Sebacate $[(CH_2)_4COOC_4H_9]_2$	(o.c.)353	26						0.963		650		1,3
Dibutyl Tartrate—n $(C_4H_9OOC)_2$-$(CHOH)_2$	195 195	26	544	26				1.098	9.03	650		1,2,3
Dichlorobenzene—o $C_6H_4Cl_2$	151	26	1198	17				1.325	5.07	354		1,2,3
Dichlorobenzene—p $C_6H_4Cl_2$	150 153 150	13 26						1.458	5.07	345		1,2,3
Dichlorobutane—1,4 CH_2ClCH_2-CH_2CH_2Cl	126	95						1.141	4.4	311		2,3
1,3—Dichlorobutene—2 $CH_2ClCH.CClCH_3$	80 80 (o.c.)75	14;26 14;26							4.31	258		2,3
Dichloroethylene—1,1 $CH_2:CCl_2$ (Dichlorethylene)	57 57 63	26 1;13	856	26;39	5.6 5.6 10	11.4 11.4 13	26;39 5	1.250	3.35	98.6		1,2,3
Dichloroethylene—1,2 $ClCH:CHCl$	43	26			9.7	12.8	26	1.282	3.35	141		1,2,3
Dichloroethyl Ether—sym $CH_2ClCH_2OCH_2$-CH_2Cl (Chlorex)	131	26	696	26				1.22	4.93	352		1,2,3
Dichloromethyl Formal $CH_2(OCH_2CHCl)_2$	(o.c.)230	26;83						1.233	5.90	424		1,2,3
1,3—Dichloro-2,4—Hexadiene $CH_2ClCH:CClCH.$:$CHCH_3$	168 168 (o.c.)180	14;26 14;26							5.20			1,2,3
Dichloroisopropyl Ether $ClCH_2CH(CH_3)OCH.$(Cl)$_2CH_3Cl$	(o.c.)185	26						1.113		369		1,2,3
1,1—Dichloro, 1—Nitro Ethane $CH_3CCl_2NO_2$	(o.c.)160	76						1.405	4.97	255		1,3
1,1—Dichloro, 1—Nitro Propane $C_2H_5CCl_2NO_2$	(o.c.)151	76						1.314	5.45	289		1,3
Dichloropentanes (Mixed) $C_5H_{10}Cl_2$	(o.c.)106	26						1.06-1.08		266		1,2,3
Dichlorostyrene $C_6H_5CCl:CHCl$	(o.c.)225	84										1,2,3
Dicyclohexylamine $(C_6H_{11})_2NH$	(o.c.)>210	26						0.910	6.27	496		3
Diethanolamine $(HOCH_2CH_2)_2NH$	(o.c.)280	12;26	1224	26				1.097	3.65	514		1,3
Diethyl Amine $(C_2H_5)_2NH$	<0	70	594	17				0.710	2.53	134		3

	FLASH POINT Deg. F.	Ref.	IGNITION TEMP. Deg. F.	Ref.	EXPLOSIVE LIMITS Per Cent by Volume Lower	Upper	Ref.	Sp. Gr. (Water = 1)	Vapor Density Air = 1	Boiling Point Deg. F.	Und. Lab. Class	Ext. Agt.
Diethylaminoethanol $(C_2H_5)_2NCH_2CH_2OH$	(o.c.)140	26						0.885	4.04	322		3
Diethyl Benzene—1,4 $C_6H_4(C_2H_5)_2$			806	17				4.62	0.86	360		3
Diethyl Carbitol $CH_3(CH_2OCH_2)_3CH_3$	(o.c.)180	26						0.908		367		1,3
Diethyl Carbonate $(C_2H_5)_2CO_3$	77	13;26						0.977	4.07	259		2,3
Diethyl Cellosolve $C_2H_5OCH_2$-$CH_2OC_2H_5$	(o.c.)95	26	406	26				0.842		251		3
Diethyl Diphenyl Urea $[(C_2H_5)(C_6H_5)N]_2CO$	302	13;26						1.12		620		1,2,3
Diethylene Glycol $CH_2OHCH_2OCH_2$-CH_2OH	255 286 255	12 26	444	11;26				1.119	3.66	472		1,3
Diethylene Oxide	See Dioxane—1,4											
Diethylene Triamine $NH_2CH_2CH_2NHCH_2$-CH_2NH_2	(o.c.)215	26	750	26				0.954	3.48	404		1
Diethyl Ether	See Ethyl Ether											
Diethyl Glycol Phthalate $C_6H_4[COO(CH_2)_2$-$OC_2H_5]_2$	343	13;26						1.11				1,3
Diethylhexylamine $[C_4H_9CH(C_2H_5)$-$CH_2]_2NH$	(o.c.)270	26;83						0.806	8.33	538		1,2,3
Diethyl Maleate $(—CHCO_2C_2H_5)_2$	(o.c.)250	65						1.064	6.0	438		
Diethyl Malonate $CH_2(COOC_2H_5)_2$ (Ethyl Malonate)	(o.c.)200	26						1.055	5.5	390		1,3
Diethyl Oxalate $(COOC_2H_5)_2$	168	26						1.07	5.03	356		1,2,3
Diethyl Pentane—3,3 CH_3CH_2C-$(C_2H_5)_2CH_2CH_3$			612	17								2,3
Diethyl Phthalate—o $C_6H_4(COOC_2H_5)_2$	243	26						1.110	7.66	576		1,2,3
Diethyl Phthalate—p $C_6H_4(COOC_2H_5)_2$	(o.c.)325	26;86						1.117-1.121	7.66	565		1,2,3
Diethyl Selenide $(C_2H_5)_2Se$					2.5		26	1.23	4.73	226		1,2,3
Diethyl Sulfate $(C_2H_5)_2SO_4$	220	12;26	817	26				1.184	5.31	406		1,2,3
Diglycol Chlorformate	(o.c.)295	26										1,2,3
Diglycol Chlorohydrin $HOCH_2CH_2OCH_2$-CH_2Cl	(o.c.)225	26						1.172		387		1,3
Diglycol Dilevulinate $\{CH_2CH_2OOC$-$\{CH_2)_2COCH_3\}_2O$	340	26						1.145				1,2,3

	FLASH POINT		IGNITION TEMP.		EXPLOSIVE LIMITS Per Cent by Volume			Sp. Gr. (Water =1)	Vapor Density Air=1	Boiling Point Deg. F.	Und. Lab. Class	Ext. Agt.
	Deg. F.	Ref.	Deg. F.	Ref.	Low-er	Up-per	Ref.					
Dihydropyran	4	26						0.923		186		
Di-isopropanolamine [CH₃CH(OH)CH₂]₂NH	(o.c.)260	26;83						0.989	4.59	108		1,3
Di-isopropyl Benzene [(CH₃)₂CH]₂C₆H₄	(o.c.)170	26	840	26					5.59			1,2,3
1,2—Dimethoxy Ethane CH₃O(CH₂)₂OCH₃ (Ethylene Glycol Dimethyl Ether)	104	96						0.869	3.1	174 @630 m.m.		3
Dimethoxy Methane CH₂(OCH₃)₂ (Formal; Methylal)	(o.c.)0	97						0.86	2.6	111		3
Dimethoxy Tetraglycol CH₃OCH₂(CH₂-OCH₂)₃CH₂OCH₃	(o.c.)285	26						1.013		528		1,3
Dimethyl Aminoethanol (CH₃)₂NCH₂CH₂OH (Dimethylethanolamine)	88 (o.c.)88 (o.c.)130	26 98						0.887	3.07	272		3
Dimethyl Aniline C₆H₅N(CH₃)₂ C.P.	145 142 145 165	13 26 28	700 700-750 700	28 26				0.956	4.17	379	20-25	1,2,3
Dimethyl Butane—2,2 (CH₃)₃CCH₂CH₃ (Neohexane)			797	17				0.649	3.00	121		3
Dimethyl Butane—2,3 (CH₃)₂CHCH(CH₃)₂ (Di-isopropyl)	<—20 (o.c.)	26;89	788	52				0.672	3.00	256		3
Dimethyl Carbinol	See Propyl Alcohol—iso.											
Dimethyl Chloracetal ClCH₂CH(OCH₃)₂	111	99	450	26				1.082-1.092	4.3	259-270		3
Dimethyl Cyclohexane— p (CH₃)₂C₆H₁₀	52	13;76						0.77	3.86	248		2,3
Dimethyldichlorosilane (DDS)					3.4	>9.5	26					
Dimethylethanolamine (CH₃)₂NC₂H₄OH	(o.c.)88	26;83						0.887	3.07	272		3
Dimethyl Ether	See Methyl Ether											
Dimethyl Ethyl Carbinol	See Amyl Alcohol—Tertiary											
Dimethyl Formamide (CH₃)₂NCHO	136	26	833		2.2 26 @212°		26	0.945		307		1,2,3
Dimethyl Glycol Phthalate C₆H₄(COO(CH₂)₂-OCH₃)₂	369	13;76						1.17	9.72	446		1,3
Dimethyl Hexane—2,3 CH₃CH(CH₃)CH-(CH₃)C₂H₅CH₃			820	17				0.724	3.9	237		
Dimethyl Maleate (—CHCOOCH₃)₂	(o.c.)235	65						1.1606	5.0	393		2,3
Dimethyl Pentane—2,3 CH₃CH(CH₃)CH-(CH₃)CH₂CH₃			639	17				3.45	0.696	193		2,3

	FLASH POINT Deg. F.	Ref.	IGNITION TEMP. Deg. F.	Ref.	EXPLOSIVE LIMITS Per Cent by Volume Low-er	Up-per	Ref.	Sp. Gr. (Water =1)	Vapor Density Air=1	Boiling Point Deg. F.	Und. Lab. Class	Ext. Agt.
Dimethyl Phthalate—o C6H4(COOCH3)2	295 290 270 295	12 13;15 26	1032	26				1.189	6.69	540		1,2,3
Dimethyl Propane—2,2 (CH3)4C			842	17				2.48	0.613	49		
Dimethyl Sulfate (CH3)2SO4	182	26						1.332	4.35	370		1,2,3
Dimethyl Sulfide (CH3)2S			403	17				0.846	2.14	100		
Dinitro Aniline—2,4 (NO2)2C6H3NH2	435	26		.				1.615	6.31			1,3
Dinitro Benzene—1,2 C6H4(NO2)2 (o—Dinitrobenzol)	302	1;13;26						1.59	5.79	605		1,3
Dinitro Chlorobenzene C6H3Cl(NO2)2	382 369 382	1;13 26			1.97	22	2;25;35	1.68	6.98			1,3
Dinitro Toluene—2,4 (NO2)2C6H3CH3								1.52	6.27	572		1,3
Dioctyl Phthalate C6H4(CO2CH2-CH(C2H5)C4H9)2	(o.c.)390	26						0.986	13.45	726		1,2,3
Dioxane—1,4 OCH2CH2OCH2CH2 (Diethylene Oxide)	54 65 54	12;26 16	356	26	1.97	22.2	16;26	1.035	3.03	214 Note: See Table of Common Hazardous Chemicals.		1,3
Dioxolane OCH2CH2OCH2	(o.c.)35	26;83						1.065	2.55	165		3
Diphenyl C6H5C6H5 (Phenyl Benzene)	235	26						0.985	5.31	491		1,3
Diphenylamine (C6H5)2NH (Phenyl Aniline)	307	13;26	846	17				1.16	5.82	575		1,3
Diphenyl Methane (C6H5)2CH2	. 266	13;26						1.006	5.79	508		1,2,3
Diphenyl Oxide (C6H5)2O (Diphenyl Ether)	239	13;26						1.073	5.86	500		1,2,3
Diphenyl Phthalate C6H4(COOC6H5)2	435	56						1.28	11.0	761		1,3
Dipropylamine—iso [(CH3)2CH]2NH	20	26						0.726		180		1,3
Dipropylene Glycol [CH3CHOHCH2]2O	(o.c.)280	26						1.040		372		1,3
Di-ter-butyl Peroxide (CH3)3COOC(CH3)3	(o.c.)65	100						0.800	5.04	232		3
Divinyl Ether CH2CHOCHCH2	<—22	26	680	26;44	1.85 1.7 1.85	36.5 27.0 36.5	26 80	0.774	2.41	102 Note: See Table of Common Hazardous Chemicals, Vinyl Ether.		3
Dodecane CH3(CH2)10CH3	165	26	993	52	0.6		26	0.750	5.86	421		1,2,3
Ester Gum	375	26								495		1,3

	FLASH POINT Deg. F.	Ref.	IGNITION TEMP. Deg. F.	Ref.	EXPLOSIVE LIMITS Per Cent by Volume Low-er	Up-per	Ref.	Sp. Gr. (Water =1)	Vapor Density Air=1	Boiling Point Deg. F.	Und. Lab. Class	Ext. Agt.
Ethane C_2H_6	Gas		950 968-1166 950 959	 31 27;26 17	3.2 3.3 3.0 3.2	12.5 10.6 15.0 12.5	 26;27;31 | 5;12	1.035		—128		4
Ethanol	See Ethyl Alcohol											
Ether	See Ethyl Ether											
Ethanolamine $NH_2CH_2CH_2OH$	185 (o.c.)200 185	12;26 101						1.02	2.10	342		1,3
Ethoxytriglycol $C_2H_5O(C_2H_4O)_3H$	275	102						1.021	6.14	492		1,3
Ethyl Acetanilide $CH_3CON(C_2H_5)(C_6H_5)$	126	13;26						0.942	5.62	400		2,3
Ethyl Acetate $CH_3COOC_2H_5$	24 24 24 28	 26 20;42 28	800 800 925 903 907	 28 11 26	2.2 2.5 2.18	11.5 11.5 11.5	 5 26	0.899	3.04	171	85 90	3
Ethyl Acetoacetate $C_2H_5CO_2CH_2COCH_3$	184 (o.c.)184 (o.c.)185	12;26 66						1.03	4.48	356		1,3
Ethyl Alcohol C_2H_5OH (Grain Alcohol, Cologne Spirits, Ethanol)	55 52 53-54 54 55 57	 13 3 6;10 18;26 43	793 822 815 700-800 799 793	 25 22 28 26 50	3.5 3.7 4 3.5 3.28 3.01 @ 212°	19 13.7 19 19.0 19	 31 5 28 26 50	0.79	1.59	173	70	3
Ethyl Alcohol and Water 96% 95% 80% 70% 60% 50% 40% 30% 20% 10% 5%	62 63 68 70 72 75 79 85 97 120 144	43 43 6 6 6 6 6 6 6 6 6										
Ethyl Amine $C_2H_5NH_2$ 70% aqueous solution	<0	26	723	17				0.778-0.802				3
Ethyl Aniline $C_6H_5NHC_2H_5$	(o.c.)185	26;94						0.95-0.97	4.17	401		1,2,3
Ethyl Benzene $C_2H_5C_6H_5$ (Phenyl Ethane)	59	26	870	26				0.868	3.66	277		2,3

	FLASH POINT Deg. F.	Ref.	IGNITION TEMP. Deg. F.	Ref.	EXPLOSIVE LIMITS Per Cent by Volume Lower	Upper	Ref.	Sp. Gr. (Water =1)	Vapor Density Air=1	Boiling Point Deg. F.	Und. Lab. Class	Ext. Agt.
Ethyl Benzoyl Acetate C₆H₅COCH₂-COOC₂H₅	(o.c.)285	26;86						1.111		291-298		1,3
Ethyl Borate (C₂H₅)₃BO₃	52	26						0.863		233		3
Ethyl Bromide C₂H₅Br (Bromo Ethane)			952	26	6.0	11.0	26	1.430	3.76	100		1,3
2—Ethyl Butyl Acetate CH₃COOCH₂CH-(C₂H₅)₂	(o.c.)130	26						0.880		324		2,3
Ethyl Butyl Alcohol (C₂H₅)₂CHCH₂OH	137	26						0.818	3.52	275		3
Ethyl Butyl Carbonate—2 (C₃H₆)(C₄H₆)CO₃	122	26						0.92	5.03	275		2,3
2—Ethyl Butyl Cellosolve (C₂H₅)₂CHCH₂-OCH₂CH₂OH	(o.c.)180	26						0.895		386		1,2,3
Ethylbutyraldehyde (C₂H₅)₂CHCHO (Diethyl Acetaldehyde)	(o.c.)70	26;83						0.816	3.45	242		3
Ethyl Butyrate—n CH₃CH₂CH₂-COOC₂H₅	78	26	865	48				0.879	4.00	248		3
Ethyl Butyric Acid (C₂H₅)₂CHCOOH (Diethyl Acetic Acid)	(o.c.)210	26;83						0.922	4.01	380		1,3
Ethyl Chloride C₂H₅Cl (Chloroethane)	—58	26	966 966 921	39 17	3.7 3.6 3.7 4.0 3.6	12.0 11.2 12.0 15 12	33 39 5 26	0.910	2.22	54		3
Ethyl Chloroformate ClCOOC₂H₅ (Ethyl Chlorocarbonate)	61 61 (o.c.)82	26;86 26;86						1.13	3.74	201		3
Ethyl Crotonate CH₃CHCHCOOC₂H₅	36	26						0.920		282		2,3
Ethyl Cyclobutane C₂H₅C₄H₇			412	17								
Ethyl Cyclohexane C₂H₅C₆H₁₁			504	17				0.782				
Ethyl Cyclopentane C₂H₅C₅H₉			504	17				0.766				
Ethyl Diethanolamine C₂H₅N(C₂H₄OH)₂	(o.c.)255	26;94						1.02	4.59	473		1,3
Ethylene C₂H₄ (Ethene)	Gas		842 1008-1018 1071-1110 1009 842 914	31 6 26 16 107	2.75 3.0 3.02 2.75	28.6 29 34 28.6	5 12;26 16		0.975	—155 Note: See Table of Common Hazardous Chemicals.		4
Ethylene Chlorhydrin (Anhydrous) HOCH₂CH₂Cl (Glycol Chlorohydrin)	(o.c.)140	12;26	797	52				1.213	2.78	264		1,3

	FLASH POINT Deg. F.	Ref.	IGNITION TEMP. Deg. F.	Ref.	EXPLOSIVE LIMITS Per Cent by Volume Lower	Upper	Ref.	Sp. Gr. (Water =1)	Vapor Density Air=1	Boiling Point Deg. F.	Und. Lab. Class	Ext. Agt.
Ethylene Diamine (Anhydrous) H₂NCH₂CH₂NH₂ 69%	93 160	12;26 26						0.890	2.07	241		3
Ethylene Dichloride CH₂ClCH₂Cl	56 58 57 56	 37 38 26	775	26	6.2 6.2 6.2	15.9 16 15.9	5 26	1.258	3.42	183	60-70	1,2,3
Ethylene Glycol CH₂OHCH₂OH (Glycol)	232 232 241	 26 12	775 775 781	25;26 11	3.2		26	1.113	2.14	387		3
Ethylene Glycol Monoacetate CH₂OHCH₂OOCCH₃	(o.c.)215	26						1.109		357		1,3
Ethylene Imine NHCH₂CH₂			612	17.				0.832	1.48	131		
Ethylene Oxide CH₂OCH₂	<0 <20 <0	 12 26	804 806 804	 29;38 26	3.0	80	5;26;29	0.887	1.52	51	100	3
Ethyl Ethanolamine C₂H₅NHC₂H₄OH	(o.c.)160	26;94						0.92	3.00	322		1,3
Ethyl Ether C₂H₅OC₂H₅ (Diethyl Ether)	—49 0 or less —49 —4 —42 to —4 —42 0 <20 <10 —4 —20	 2 22;28 6 1 13 18 12 43 7 26	356 356 649 370 366	16;22;- 28 31 11;25 26	1.35 1.9 3.0 1.5 1.8 1.7 1.0 1.6 2.9 1.85	36.5 22 7.5 48 5.2 48 6 7.7 7.5 36.5	28;29 22 1 5;11;26 7 31 6 16	0.71	2.55	95	100	3
Ethyl Formate HCO₂C₂H₅	—4 —4 —3	 13;26 1	1071	52	2.75 3.5 2.75	16.4 16.5 16.4	5;26 81	0.922	2.55	130		2,3
Ethyl Glycol	See Cellosolve											
Ethylhexaldehyde C₄H₉CH(C₂H₅)CHO	(o.c.)125	26;83						0.820	4.42	325		2,3
2—Ethylhexanediol—1,3 C₂H₇CH(OH)CH·(C₂H₅)CH₂OH	(o.c.)260	26;83						0.942	5.03	472		1,2,3
2—Ethylhexanoic Acid C₄H₉CH(C₂H₅)COOH	(o.c.)260	26;83						0.907	4.97	440		1,2,3
Ethylhexanol C₄H₉CH(C₂H₅)-CH₂OH	(o.c.)185	26;83						0.834	4.49	359		1,2,3
Ethylhexyl Acetate CH₃COOCH₂CH-(C₂H₅)C₄H₉ (Octyl Acetate)	(o.c.)190	26;83						0.885	5.93	410		1,2,3

Note: See Table of Common Hazardous Chemicals.

The wide variation in flash point figures for ethyl ether may be explained by the fact that special equipment is necessary to determine its flash point with any reasonable degree of accuracy. The theoretical calculated flash point is —49°.

	FLASH POINT Deg. F.	Ref.	IGNITION TEMP. Deg. F.	Ref.	EXPLOSIVE LIMITS Per Cent by Volume Low-er	Up-per	Ref.	Sp. Gr. (Water =1)	Vapor Density Air=1	Boiling Point Deg. F.	Und. Lab. Class	Ext. Agt.
Ethylhexylamine C₄H₉CH(C₂H₅)-CH₂NH₂	(o.c.)140	104						0.789	4.45	337		1,3
Ethylidene Dichloride CH₃CHCl₂	22	105						1.17	3.4	135-138		3
Ethyl Lactate CH₃CHOHCOOC₂H₅ Tech.	115 117 115 131	13 26 58	752		1.55 50 @ 212°		50	1.03	4.07	309	30-35	3
Ethyl Mercaptan C₂H₅SH	<80	26	570	72	2.8	18.2	72	0.839	2.11	98		3
Ethyl Methyl Ether CH₃OC₂H₅	—35	26	374	26	2.0	10.1	26	0.697	2.07	50		3
Ethyl Methyl Ketone C₂H₅COCH₃	30 30 21	18;26 58	960 960 941	26 58	1.81 2.0 1.81 1.70 @ 212°	11.5 12 11.5	5 26 50	0.805	2.48	176	85-90	3
Ethyl Morpholine CH₂CH₂OC₂H₄N-CH₂CH₃	(o.c.)89.6	26;83						0.916	4.00	280		2,3
Ethyl Nitrate CH₃CH₂ONO₂	50	26			3.8		5;26	1.105	3.14	190		2,3
Ethyl Nitrite C₂H₅NO₂	—31	26	194	18	3.0	>50	5;26	0.900	2.59	63		2,3
Ethyl Oxalate (COOC₂H₅)₂ (Oxalic Ether)	168	43						1.080	5.04	367		1,3
Ethyl Phthallyl Ethyl Glycollate C₂H₅OCOC₆H₄-OCOCH₂OCOC₂H₅	365 365 386	26 56						1.180	9.6	608		1,2,3
Ethyl Propionate C₂H₅COOC₂H₅	54 54 55-60	13;26 14	890 890 824	72 17				0.891	3.52	210		2,3
2—Ethyl—3— Propyl Acrolein C₃H₇CH:C(C₂H₅)-CHO (2—Ethyl Hexenal)	(o.c.)155	26;83						0.851	4.35	347		1,2,3
Ethyl Silicate (C₂H₅)₄SiO₄	(o.c.)125	66						0.936	7.22	334		3
Ethyl p—Toluene Sulfonamide C₇H₇SO₂NHC₂H₅	260	26						1.253	5.6	208 @745 m.m.		1,3
Ethyl p—Toluene Sulfonate C₇H₇SO₂C₂H₅	316	13;26										1,2,3
Ethyltrichloro Silane CH₃CH₂SiCl₃	(o.c.)72	57						1.239	5.6	208 @745 m.m.		3
Fish Oil	420	9										1,2,3
Flavoring Extracts	<80	2										3

	FLASH POINT Deg. F.	Ref.	IGNITION TEMP. Deg. F.	Ref.	EXPLOSIVE LIMITS Per Cent by Volume Low-er	Up-per	Ref.	Sp. Gr. (Water =1)	Vapor Density Air=1	Boiling Point Deg. F.	Und. Lab. Class	Ext. Agt.
Formaldehyde CH₂O			806	26	7.0 7.0 7	73 73	26 106		1.075		—6	4
37%	130 185	26 88	817	26					1.03			3
Formic Acid HCOOH	156	26	1114	84				1.218	1.59	213		1,3
Fuel Oil No. 1 (Kerosene) (Range Oil) (Coal Oil)	100 Min. or Legal	108	490	26				<1	Note: The legal minimum flash point for kerosene varies in different states. The flash point is usually above 100°F.			2,3
Fuel Oil No. 2 (Diesel Oil)	100 Min. or Legal	108	494	26				<1				2,3
Fuel Oil No. 4	130 Min. or Legal	108	505	26				<1	Note: Commercial Standard CS 12-48, U. S. Bureau of Stds., gives further details. Fuel Oil No. 3 is no longer a current standard.			1,2,3
Fuel Oil No. 5	130 Min. or Legal	108						<1				1,2,3
Fuel Oil No. 6	150 Min. or Legal	108	765	26				1±				1,2,3
Furfural C₄H₃OCHO (Fural)	140 143 140	28 26	600 600-675 739	28 26	2.1 2. 2.1		5 26	1.159	3.31	322	25-30	1,2,3
Furfuryl Alcohol C₄H₃OCH₂OH	167	26	915	26				1.129	3.37	340		3
Fusel Oil (See also Amyl Alcohol)	108	43										3
Gas, Blast Furnace					35	74	5;26					4
Gas, Coal Gas			1200 1200 1197-1200	26 6	5.3	31	5;26					4
Gas, Illuminating			1094	26;30; 39	5.3 5.3 6.0	31 31 30	6;26 30					4
Gas, Natural					4.8	13.5	5;26					4
Gas, Oil Gas			637	26	6.0	13.5	26					4
Gas, Producer					20.7	73.7	26					4
Gas, Water					9.0 6.9 9.0	55.0 55-70 55.0	5 26					4
Gas Oil	150 175-230 150+	7 26	640	26	6.0	13.5	26	<1				1,2,3
Gasoline C₆H₁₂ to C₉H₂₀	—45 —45 to 0 0 —50	28 22 26	495 515 536 570 495	25 28 21 26 @ 212°	1.3 1.4 1.3 0.94	6.0 6.0 6.0	22;28 26 50	0.75	3-4	100-400	95-100	2,3
								Note: Values may vary considerably for different grades of gasoline.				
(74-76 A.P.I.) (100 Octane) (56 to 60 Octane)	—45 —36 —45	28 109 109	853 536	109 109	1.1 1.3		109 109					

	FLASH POINT Deg. F.	Ref.	IGNITION TEMP. Deg. F.	Ref.	EXPLOSIVE LIMITS Per Cent by Volume Lower	Upper	Ref.	Sp. Gr. (Water = 1)	Vapor Density Air = 1	Boiling Point Deg. F.	Und. Lab. Class	Ext. Agt.
Gasoline (Casinghead)	0 or less	2										
Gin (See Ethyl Alcohol and Water) (Dutch)	89	40										
Glycerine HOCH2CHOHCH2-OH (Glycerol)	320 350 320	28 26	739 739 650-750	26 28				1.26	3.17	554	10-20	1,3
Glyceryl Triacetate (C3H5)(OOCCH3)a (Triacetin)	280	26	812	26				1.161	7.52	496		1,2,3
Glycol Diacetate (CH2OOCCH3)2 (Ethylene Acetate)	(o.c.)220	26						1.100	5.03	370		1,2,3
Glycol Diformate HCOOCH2CH2-OCOH	(o.c.)200	26;83						1.227	4.07	345		1,3
Heptadecanol C4H9CH(C2H5)C2H4-CH(OH)C2H4CH-(C2H5)2	(o.c.)310	26;83						0.847	8.84	590		1,2,3
Heptane—n CH3(CH2)5CH3	25 30 25	13 26	452 452 461 432	26 11 17	1.4 1.4 1.0 0.95	7.2 7.2 6.0 3.6	93 26 11	0.683	3.45	208		2,3
Heptane-iso (Mixture of Heptane Isomers)	<0	26			1.0	6.0	26	0.725	3.45	176-195		2,3
Heptanol—2 CH3(CH2)4CH-(OH)CH3	(o.c.)160	26;83						0.818	4.01	320		1,2,3
Hexachlorobenzene C6Cl6 (Perchlorbenzene)	468	42						1.5	9.8	617		3
Hexane—n CH3(CH2)4CH3	—15 —7 —24 to 0 —15	26 13 28	500 490 477 500-565 502	25 26 28 50 @ 212°	1.2 1.25 1.1 0.90	6.90 6.90 4.2	26 11 50	0.661	2.97	156	90-95	3
Hexane—iso (Mixture of Hexane Isomers)	<—20	26			1.0	7.0	84	0.669	3.00	134-142		2,3
Hexanediol—2,5 CH3CH(OH)CH2-CH2CH(OH)CH3 (2,5—Dihydroxy Hexane)	230	102						0.962	4.07	429		2,3
Hexyl Acetate (CH3)2CH(CH2)3-OOCCH3 (Methyl Amyl Acetate)	113	12;26						0.855	4.97	285		3
Hexyl Alcohol—n CH3(CH2)4CH2OH (Hexanol—1)	145	12;26						0.82	3.52	311		3
Hexylene Glycol CH2OHCHOH-(CH2)3CH3	(o.c.)205	26						0.922	4.07	385		1,2,3
Hexyl Ether C6H13OC6H13	(o.c.)170	26;83						0.794	6.43	440		1,2,3

	FLASH POINT Deg. F.	Ref.	IGNITION TEMP. Deg. F.	Ref.	EXPLOSIVE LIMITS Per Cent by Volume Low-er	Up-per	Ref.	Sp. Gr. (Water =1)	Vapor Density Air=1	Boiling Point Deg. F.	Und. Lab. Class	Ext. Agt.
Hydrazine H₂NNH₂			518	17				1.011	1.1	236		
Hydrocyanic Acid HCN (Prussic Acid) (Hydrogen Cyanide)	0	26	1000	26	6 / 5.6 / 12.75 / 6	40 / 40 / 27 / 40	26:28 / 5;34 / 16	0.697	0.932 Note: See Table of Common Hazardous Chemicals.	79		1,4
Hydrogen H₂	Gas		1085 / 1076-1094 / 1085 / 1076	30;31 / 5 / 26	4.1 / 4.1 / 4.1 / 4.1	74.2 / 75 / 74 / 74.2	1 / 5 / 26		0.069	—422		4
Hydrogen Sulfide H₂S	Gas		500 / 482-534	1	4.3 / 4.3 / 4.3	46 / 46 / 45.5	5 / 26	1.189	Note: See Table of Common Hazardous Chemicals.	—76		4
Hydroquinone C₆H₄(OH)₂	329	1;13;26	960	26				1.332	3.81	545		1,3
Hydroxyethyl Morpholine C₂H₄OC₂H₄NC₂-H₄OH	(o c)210	83;84						1.072	4.52	437		3
Hydroxylamine NH₂OH (Oxammonium)	Explodes @ 265°	26						1.227		158		
Isoprene CH₂:C(CH₂)CH:CH₂	—65.2	92	428	92				0.679	2.35	93		3
Kerosene (Fuel Oil No. 1)	100-165 / 100 Minimum / 100-165	108 / 26	490 / 482 / 490 / 439	22;28 / 26 / 17	1.16	6.0	26	<1	4.5 / 4 to 8		40	2,3
Lacquer	0-80	2										3
Lactol Spirits	7 or less	20	590	20								3
Lanolin (Wool Grease)	460	26	833	26				<1				1,2,3
Lard Oil (Commercial or animal) No. 1	363 / 398 / 440 / 363 / 395	9 / 9 / 28 / 26	650 / 650-750 / 033	23 / 26				<1			10-20	1,2,3
Lard Oil (Pure) No. 2 Mineral	500 / 494 / 530-600 / 419 / 404	9 / 3 / 3 / 9										1,2,3
Lauryl Bromide CH₃(CH₂)₁₀CH₂Br (Dodecyl Bromide)	291	111						1.021				1
Lead Tetramethyl Pb(CH₃)₄					1.8		5;26	1.995	9.20	230		1,2,3
Leather Cement	0 or less	2										2,3
Leather Dressing	<80	2										2,3

	FLASH POINT Deg. F.	Ref.	IGNITION TEMP. Deg. F.	Ref.	EXPLOSIVE LIMITS Per Cent by Volume Low-er	Up-per	Ref.	Sp. Gr. (Water =1)	Vapor Density Air=1	Boiling Point Deg. F.	Und. Lab. Class	Ext. Agt.
Linseed Oil Raw	432		650					0.93		600+		1,2,3
	468	22	650-750	28								
	432	28	820	26								
	435	26										
Boiled	403											
	403	28										
	378	3										
Liquid Metal Polish	<80	2										2,3
Liquid Stove Polish	<80	2										2,3
Lubricating Oil, Mineral (Paraffin Oil, includes Motor Oil)	300-450	26	500-700					<1				1,2,3
Lubricating Oil, Spindle	169	112	478	1				<1				1,2,3
Lubricating Oil, Turbine	(o.c.)400	112	700	26				<1				1,2,3
Maleic Anhydride (COCH)$_2$O	(o.c.)240	26;83						1.305	3.38	396		1,3
Menhaden Oil (Pogy Oil)	435		828					0.927				1,2,3
	435	26		26								
	405	3										
Mercaptoethanol—2 HSCH$_2$CH$_2$OH	(o.c.)165	26;83						1.116	2.70	315		3
Mesityl Oxide (CH$_3$)$_2$CCHCOCH$_3$	87		652					0.858	3.40	266		3
	87	26		26								
	79	113										
Metaldehyde (C$_2$H$_4$O)$_4$	97	26							6.06			1,3
Methallyl Alcohol CH$_2$C(CH$_3$)CH$_2$OH	92	115						0.852	2.5	237		1,3
Methallyl Chloride CH$_2$C(CH$_3$)CH$_2$Cl	11	115			3.2	8.1	115	0.926	3.1	162		3
Methane CH$_4$ (Marsh Gas)	Gas		999	30;31	5.3	14.0	5;12	0.554		—258		4
			1202-1382	26;27	5.3	14.0	7					
			999	35	5.0	16.0	27					
			1193		5.6	13.5	35					
					4.9	15.0	26					
					5.3	13.9						
Methoxy Ethyl Phthalate (Methox)	275	26										1,2,3
Methoxytriglycol Acetate CH$_3$COO(C$_2$H$_4$O)$_3$-CH$_3$	(o.c.)260	26;83						1.094	7.11	266		3
Methyl Acetate CH$_3$COOCH$_3$	14		850		4.1	13.9		0.925	2.56	140	85-90	3
	14	28	942	11	4.1	14	5					
	20	12	935	26	4.1	13.9	26					
	15	26	953	25								
			850-925	28								
Methyl Acetoacetate CH$_3$CO$_2$CH$_2$COCH$_3$	170							1.077	4.00	338		1,2,3
	170	66										
	180	12										

	FLASH POINT Deg. F.	Ref.	IGNITION TEMP. Deg. F.	Ref.	EXPLOSIVE LIMITS Per Cent by Volume Low-er	Up-per	Ref.	Sp. Gr. (Water =1)	Vapor Density Air=1	Boiling Point Deg. F.	Und. Lab. Class	Ext. Agt.
Methylal $CH_3OCH_2OCH_3$ (Dimethoxy Methane) (Formal)	(o.c.)0	97						0.856	2.6	111		3
Methyl Alcohol CH_3OH (Methanol) (Wood Alcohol)	52 45 49 52 57 54	2;3 6;10 3;12 15 22;26	867 887 886 878 867	11 25 26 50	6.0 6.0 6.0 6.7 5.8 @212°	36.5 36 36.5	1 26 50 50	0.792	1.11	147	70	3
Methyl Amine CH_3NH_2 30%	0 32.5	26 116	806	52				0.699		19		3
Methyl Benzoate $C_6H_5COOCH_3$ (Niobe Oil)	181	42						1.093	4.7	302		2,3
Methyl Bromide CH_3Br	Practically non-flammable		999	39	13.5	14.5	5;26:-46	1.732	3.27	40		
Methyl Butyrate $CH_3COOC_3H_7$	57	1;13;-26						0.898	3.52	215		2,3
Methyl Carbitol $CH_3O(CH_2)_2O$-$(CH_2)_2OH$	(o.c.)200	12;26						1.035	4.11	379		1 3
Methyl Carbitol Acetate $CH_3COOC_2H_4$-$OC_2H_4OCH_3$	(o.c.)180	26						1.039		409		2,3
Methyl Cellosolve $CH_2OHCH_2OCH_3$	105 107 105	26 12	551 551 720	26 17				0.966	2.62	255		3
Methyl Cellosolve Acetate $CH_3OCH_2CH_2$-CO_2CH_3	132 132 (o.c.)140	12.26 66						1.005	4.07	289		3
Methyl Chloride CH_3Cl (Chloromethane)	Gas		1170	39	8.0 8.0 8.1	19 19 17.2	5 26;39	0.92	1.78	−11		4
Methyl Cyclohexane $CH_2(CH_2)_4CHCH_3$	25	13;26			1.15 1.2 1.15		5 26	0.770	3.38	214		2,3
Methyl Cyclohexanol $C_7H_{13}OH$ (Methyl Hexalin) (Hexahydrocresol)	154 154 160	13;26 47						0.933	3.93	329		1,2,3
Methyl Cyclohexanone $C_7H_{12}O$	118	13;26						0.925	3.86	325		2,3
Methyl Cyclohexyl Acetate $C_9H_{16}O_2$	147	13;26							5.37			2,3
Methyldiethanolamine $CH_3N(C_2H_4OH)_2$	(o.c.)260	26.83						1.042	4.11	464		3

	FLASH POINT		IGNITION TEMP.		EXPLOSIVE LIMITS Per Cent by Volume			Sp. Gr. (Water =1)	Vapor Density Air=1	Boiling Point Deg. F.	Und. Lab. Class	Ext. Agt.
	Deg. F.	Ref.	Deg. F.	Ref.	Low-er	Up-per	Ref.					
Methylene Chloride CH_2Cl_2	Practically non-flammable		1224 1224 1185	26;39 26	15.5 In Oxygen only.	66.4	67	1.336	2.93	104		1,2,3
Methyl Ether $(CH_3)_2O$ (Dimethyl Ether) (Methyl Oxide)	—42	1;26	662	52	3.45	18.1	117		1.59	—11		3
Methyl Ethyl Ether	See Ethyl Methyl Ether											
Methyl Ethyl Ketone	See Ethyl Methyl Ketone											
Methyl Formate CH_3OOCH	—2	26	840 928 853 840	35 39 26	4.5 6 5.08 4.5	22.7 20 22.7 20	5 35 26;39	0.975	2.07	90		3
2—Methyl Furan $C_4H_3OCH_3$ (Sylvan)	—22	118						0.916	2.8	144-147		3
Methyl Glycol Acetate	111	- 26							4.07			3
Methyl Lactate $(CH_3)_2CHCH_2-COOCH_3$	121	26	725		2.21 50 @ 212°		50	1.09		292		3
Methyl Monochlor Acetate $CH_2ClCOOCH_3$	116 116 (o.c.)125	26 26						1.227	3.74	269		3
Methyl Pentadiene $CH_2:CH_3CCH:-CHCH_3$	—22	119										3
2—Methyl Pentane $(CH_3)_2CH(CH_2)_2CH_3$			583	17				0.654	3.0	140		
2—Methyl—1,3—Pentanediol $CH_3CH_2CH(OH)-CH(CH_3)CH_2OH$	230	120						0.969	4.0	419		
Methyl Phthalyl Ethyl Glycollate $CH_3CO_2C_6H_4CO_2-CH_2CO_2C_2H_5$	380	56						1.220	9.2	590		1,2,3
2—Methyl Propene $CH_2:C(CH_3)CH_3$ (Butylene—iso)			869	17						20		
Methyl Propionate $CH_3COOC_2H_5$	28	1;13;26	876	17				0.915	3.03	176		2,3
Methyl Propyl Carbinol $CH_3CHOHC_3H_7$	105	7							3.03			3
Methyl iso—Propyl Carbinol $C_6H_{12}O$	103	7							3.03			3
Methyl n—Propyl Ketone $CH_3COC_3H_7$ (Pentanone—2)	(o.c.)60	26	941	52	1.55	8.15	26	0.812	2.96	216		3
Methyl Salicylate $HOC_6H_4COOCH_3$ (Oil of Wintergreen)	214 219 214	28 26	850 850-950 850	28 26				1.182	5.24	432	20-25	1,2,3
Methyl Stearate $C_{17}H_{35}COOCH_3$	307	42						0.860	10.3			

	FLASH POINT Deg. F.	Ref.	IGNITION TEMP. Deg. F.	Ref.	EXPLOSIVE LIMITS Per Cent by Volume Low-er	Up-per	Ref.	Sp. Gr. (Water =1)	Vapor Density Air = 1	Boiling Point Deg. F.	Und. Lab. Class	Ext. Agt.
Methyl Vinyl Ketone $CH_3COCHCH_2$	20 20 (o.c.)42	14:26 14:26								177		2,3
Mineral Oil	(o.c.)380	26										1,2,3
Mineral Seal Oil (Typical) (Signal Oil)	170	26										1,2,3
Mineral Spirits No. 10 (Turpentine Substitute)	104 104 85	50 26	473		0.77 50 @ 212°		50	0.80	3.9	300		2,3
Mono-Chlor-Benzol	See Chlorobenzene											
Monocresyl Diphenyl Phosphate $(C_7H_7)(C_6H_5)_2PO_4$	450	26						>1				1,2,3
Morpholine $O(CH_2CH_2)_2NH$	(o.c.)100	26:83						1.001	3.00	262		3
Mustard Oil $C_3H_5N:C:S$ (Allyl Isothiocyanate)	115	121						1.015	3.42	304		3
Naphtha, Coal Tar (High Flash Naphtha)	100-110	26	900-960	26				<1		300-400		2,3
Naphtha, Petroleum	See Benzine											
Naphtha 49° Bé	107	20	531	20								2,3
Naphtha, Safety Solvent (See Cleaning Solvents) (Stoddard Solvent)	100-110	26	450-500	26	1.1	6.0	26	<1		300-400		2,3
Naphtha V. M. & P. (76° Naphtha)	20 30 20	21 26	450 520 450-500	21 26	0.9 0.9 0.76 @212°	6.0 6.0	50 26 50	<1		212-320		2,3
Naphthalene $C_{10}H_8$ (White Tar)	176 185 174 176	16:22 26 16	1038 1053 1038	26 16	0.9 0.9	5.9 5.9	26 90	1.145	4.42	424		1,3
								Note: Melting point 176° F. See Table of Common Hazardous Chemicals.				
Naphthol-beta $C_{10}H_7OH$	307 322 307	1,13 26						1.22	4.97	547		1,3
Naphthylamine—alpha $C_{10}H_7NH_2$	315	13:26						1.171	4.93	572		1,3
Natural Gas	See Gas											
Neatsfoot Oil	470	26	828	26				0.92				1,2,3
Nicotine $C_{10}H_{14}N_2$			471	82	0.75	4.0	82	1.009	5.61	475		3
Nitroaniline—p $(NO_2)(NH_2)C_6H_4$	390	26						1.417		>545		1,3
								Note: See Table of Common Hazardous Chemicals.				
Nitrobenzol $C_6H_5NO_2$ (Nitrobenzene) (Oil of Mirbane) C.P.	190 190 188 192 198	13:26 22 13 28	900 924 900-950	26 @200° 28	1.8 @200°		26	1.2	4.25	412	20-30	1,2,3
Nitrobiphenyl—o $C_6H_5C_6H_4NO_2$	290	56						1.203	6.9	626		1,3
Nitrocellulose (Wet with solvent)	40	2										

	FLASH POINT Deg. F.	Ref.	IGNITION TEMP. Deg. F.	Ref.	EXPLOSIVE LIMITS Per Cent by Volume Low-er	Up-per	Ref.	Sp. Gr. (Water =1)	Vapor Density Air=1	Boiling Point Deg. F.	Und. Lab. Class	Ext. Agt.
Nitrochlorobenzene—p C₆H₄ClNO₂	261	1;13;26						1.52	5.43	468		1,3
								Note: See Table of Common Hazardous Chemicals				
Nitroethane C₂H₅NO₂	82 82 (o.c.)106	26 76	778	26				1.052	2.58	237		3
Nitroglycerine C₃H₅(NO₃)₃	Explodes		518	26				1.601	7.84			
Nitromethane CH₃NO₂	95	26	785	26				1.139	2.11	214		3
Nitronaphthalene—alpha C₁₀H₇NO₂	327	13;26						1.331	5.96	579		1,3
Nitropropane—1 CH₃CH₂CH₂NO₂	(o.c.)120	76	789	26				1.003	3.06	268		3
Nitropropane—2 CH₃CHNO₂CH₃	(o.c.)103	76	802	26				0.992	3.06	248		3
Nitropyridine			725	26								1,4
Nitrotoluol—p CH₃C₆H₄NO₂ (Nitrotoluene)	223	13;26						1.286	4.72	460		1,3
m—Nitro p–Toluidine C₇H₈(NH₂)(NO₂)	315	26						1.312	5.80			1,3
Nonane—n C₉H₂₀	88	26	545	52	0.74 0.83 0.74	2.9 2.9	5 11;26	0.718	4.41	302		3
Octane CH₃(CH₂)₆CH₃	60 56 63	26 1;13	450 450 527-536	26 1	0.84 0.84 0.85 1.0	3.2 3.2	11;26 4 5	0.706	3.86	257		2,3
Octane—iso (CH₃)₂CH(CH₂)₄CH₃	10	26;89	986	123				0.751	3.93	210		2,3
Octyl Acetate—n C₄H₉CHC₂H₅CH₂-CO₂CH₃	180 180 (o.c.)190	12;26 66						0.885	5.93	410		1,2,3
p—Octyl Alcohol—n CH₃(CH₂)₆CH₂OH	178	12;26						0.827	4.48	381		2,3
Octyl Aldehyde C₇H₁₅CHO	125	12;26						0.821	4.41	350		2,3
Octylene Glycol [CH₃(CH₂)₂CHOH]₂	230	26	635	26				0.939-0.943	5.05	475		1,2,3
Oleic Acid C₈H₁₇CH:CH(CH₂)₇-COOH (Red Oil) Distilled	372 364	26 3	685	26				0.891		432		1,2,3
Oleo Oil	450	26						0.915		464		1,2,3
Olive Oil (Sweet Oil)	437 485 420 437	28 10 26	650 650-800 826	28 26				0.910				1,2,3
Ozocerite (Mineral Wax)	236	26						0.95				1,3
Paint and Grease Eradicators	0-80	2										2,3

	FLASH POINT Deg. F.	Ref.	IGNITION TEMP. Deg. F.	Ref.	EXPLOSIVE LIMITS Per Cent by Volume Low-er	Up-per	Ref.	Sp. Gr. (Water =1)	Vapor Density Air=1	Boiling Point Deg. F.	Und. Lab. Class	Ext. Agt.
Paint, Bronze or Gold	0-70	2										2,3
Paint, Liquid	0-80	2										2,3
Palm Kernel Oil (Palm Nut Oil)	398	24						0.95				1,2,3
Palm Oil (Palm Butter)	323 421 323	22;26 28	600 752 600-700 650	1 28 26				0.92				1,2,3
Paraffin Oil (See also Lubricating Oil)	444 444 410	22;28 3										1,2,3
Paraffin Wax	390	26	473	26				0.9		>700		1,3
Paraformaldehyde HO(CHO)$_n$H	158 160 158	88 26	572	88								1,3
Paraldehyde (CH$_3$CHO)$_3$	63	26	460	26	1.3		26		4.55	255		1,3
Peanut Oil Cooking (Katchung Oil)	540 (o.c.)600 540	26 26	833	26				0.92				1,2,3 3
Pent-Acetate (Mixture of Isomeric Amyl Acetates and Amyl Alcohols)	98 98 (o.c.)105	26;94 26;94						0.864		260		2,3
Pentalarm (Mixture of Isomeric Amyl Mercaptans)	(o.c.)63	84;94						0.83- 0.85		212		1,3
Pentamethylene Oxide O(CH$_2$)$_4$CH$_2$ (Tetrahydropyran)	—4	124						0.854	3.0	178		3
Pentane CH$_3$(CH$_2$)$_3$CH$_3$	<—40 0 0 or less <—40	10 18 26	588 593 588 549	25 26 17	1.45 1.45 1.3 2.5 1.4	7.5 7.5 7.0 4.8 8.0	5 1 6:8 26	0.631	2.48	97		2,3
Pentane—iso (CH$_3$)$_2$CHCH$_2$CH$_3$ (?—Methyl Butane)	<—60	26;89	788	62				0.625	2.40	80- 86		2,3
Pentanedione—2,4 CH$_3$COCH$_2$COCH$_3$	(o.c.)105	26;83						0.975	3.45	284		3
Pentaphen C$_5$H$_{11}$C$_6$H$_4$OH (p—ter—Amyl Phenol)	(o.c.)232	26						0.91- 0.94				1,2,3
Pentasol (Mixture of Isomeric Amyl Alcohols)	(o.c.)113	84;94						0.81- 0.82		233- 284		2,3
Perilla Oil	522	26						0.93				1,2,3
Petrohol 98%	59	21	845	21								3
Petrohol 91%	66	21	895	21								3

	FLASH POINT Deg. F.	Ref.	IGNITION TEMP. Deg. F.	Ref.	EXPLOSIVE LIMITS Per Cent by Volume Low-er	Up-per	Ref.	Sp. Gr. (Water = 1)	Vapor Density Air = 1	Boiling Point Deg. F.	Und. Lab. Class	Ext. Agt.
Petroleum, Crude	20-90 20-90 <80	26 2						<1				2,3
Petroleum Ether	—69 —69 —50	28 26	475 624 475	28 26	1.4	5.9	26	0.64	2.50	100 100-160	95-100	2,3
Petroleum Sulfonate (Petronate)	(o.c.)400	26										1,2,3
Phenanthrene (C₆H₄CH)₂								1.063	6.14	644		1,2,3
Phenol C₆H₅OH (Carbolic Acid)	175 174 172 175	1;13;88 16;22 26	1319	26;31;88				1.07 Note: See Table of Common Hazardous Chemicals.	3.24	358		1,3
Phenyl Cellosolve C₆H₅O(CH₂)₂OH	(o.c.)250	26						1.109		473		3
Phenyldiethanolamine C₆H₅N(C₂H₄OH)₂	(o.c.)375	26;83						1.120				1,3
Phenylene Diamine—p C₆H₄(NH₂)₂	312	26							3.72	512		1,3
Phenylethanolamine C₆H₅NHC₂H₄OH	(o.c.)305	26;83						1.097		545		1,2,3
Phenyl Ethyl Alcohol C₆H₅CH₂CH₂OH (Benzyl Carbinol)	216	13;26						1.024	4.21	430		1,2,3
Phenylhydrazine C₆H₅NHNH₂	192	125						1.097	3.7	Decomposes		
Phenylmethyl Ketone	See Acetophenone											
Phorone (CH₃)₂CCHCOCHC(CH₃)₂	(o.c.)185	26						0.879		388		1,2,3
Phorone—iso COCHC(CH₃)CH₂C(CH₃)₂CH₂	(o.c.)205	26;83	864	52				0.923	4.77	419		1,3
Phosphorus (Red)			500	26				2.30 Note: See Table of Common Hazardous Chemicals.				1
Phosphorus (Yellow)			86	26				1.82 Note: See Table of Common Hazardous Chemicals.		549		1
Phosphorus Sesquisulfide P₄S₃			212	26				2.03 Note: See Table of Common Hazardous Chemicals.		765		1
Phthalic Anhydride C₆H₄(CO)₂O	305	26	1083 1083 1076	26 126	1.7	10.4	126	1.527	5.10	543		1,3
Picoline-alpha CH₃C₅H₄N (Alpha Methyl Pyridine)	(o.c.)85	26	1000	26						262		3
Picric Acid (NO₂)₃C₆H₂(OH) (Trinitrophenol)	Explodes		<572	26				1.763 Note: See Table of Common Hazardous Chemicals.	7.90			1
Pinene—alpha C₁₀H₁₆	91	26						0.86		312		2,3
Pine Oil Steam Distilled	172 138 148 172	7 7 26						0.86				1,2,3

	FLASH POINT Deg. F.	Ref.	IGNITION TEMP. Deg. F.	Ref.	EXPLOSIVE LIMITS Per Cent by Volume Lower	Upper	Ref.	Sp. Gr. (Water =1)	Vapor Density Air=1	Boiling Point Deg. F.	Und. Lab. Class	Ext. Agt.
Pine Pitch	285,	26	Note: Melting point 148° F.							490		1,3
Pine Resin (Colophony)	370	26						1.08				1,3
Pine Tar	130	26	671	26						208		2,3
Pine Tar Oil (Wood Tar Oil)	144 135 144	7 26						0.862				3
Piperidine $(CH_2)_5NH$ (Hexahydropyridine)	61	42						0.868	3.0	223		3
Polyamyl Naphthalene (Mixture of Polymers)	(o.c.)360	26;94						0.92-0.93				1,2,3
Polyethylene Glycol 200 (Mixture of Polymers)	(o.c.)350	26;83						1.12				1,3
Polyethylene Glycol 300 (Mixture of Polymers)	(o.c.)385	26;83						1.13				1,3
Polyethylene Glycol 400 (Mixture of Polymers)	(o.c.)435	26;83						1.13				1,3
Polyethylene Glycol 600 (Mixture of Polymers)	(o.c.)475	26;83						1.13				1,3
Polyvinyl Alcohol (Mixture of Polymers)	(o.c.)175	26										1,3
Potassium Xanthate $C_2H_5OCS_2K$	205	26				9.5	26	1.558				1,3
Propanal CH_3CH_2CHO (Propionaldehyde)	(o.c.)15-19	127						0.805	2.0	120		3
Propane $CH_3CH_2CH_3$	Gas		871 871 957-1090 919	7;27;-26 1 52	2.37 2.3 2.4 2.4	9.5 7.3 9.5 9.5	7;22;-39 4 5;12		1.56	—45		4
Propanol	See Propyl Alcohol											
Propanolamine—iso $CH_3CH(OH)CH_2NH_2$	(o.c.)160	26.83						0.962	2.58	318		1,3
Propionic Anhydride $(CH_3CH_2CO)_2O$	(o.c.)165	26;83						1.012	4.49	337		1,3
Propionyl Chloride CH_3CH_2COCl (Propanoyl Chloride)	54	42						1.061	3.2	176		3
Propyl Acetate—n $C_2H_5OOCCH_3$	58	1;26	842	52	1.77 2.0	8.0	26;81	0.886	3.52	215		2,3
Propyl Acetate—iso $(CH_3)_2CHOOCCH_3$	40 40 39 43 35	1 13 26 12	860 862 860 889	11 26 17	1.78 2.0	7.8	26;81	0.877	3.52	194		2,3
Propyl Alcohol—n $CH_3CH_2CH_2OH$ (Propanol—1)	59 73 73-114 77 72 75 59	6;7;10 1 28 13 13 26	700 809 700-800 941 818 812	11 28 31 25 26	2.15 2.5 2.15	13.5 13.5	26 81	0.804	2.07	207	55-60	3

	FLASH POINT		IGNITION TEMP.		EXPLOSIVE LIMITS Per Cent by Volume			Sp. Gr. (Water =1)	Vapor Density Air=1	Boiling Point Deg. F.	Und. Lab. Class	Ext. Agt.
	Deg. F.	Ref.	Deg. F.	Ref.	Low-er	Up-per	Ret.					
Propyl Alcohol—iso (CH₃)₂CHOH (Isopropanol) (Dimethyl Carbinol) (Propanol—2) 87.9% iso	53 54 53-58 61 70 53 57	 7 1 28 12 26 13	750 1094 750-850 858 857 852	 31 28 11 25 26	2.5		5;26	0.789	2.07	181	70	3
Propyl Amine—n CH₃(CH₂)₂NH₂			604	17				0.719	2.03	120		1,3
Propyl Amine—iso (CH₃)₂CHNH₂	(o.c.)—15	26	756	17				0.686	2.03	89		1,3
Propyl Benzene—n C₃H₇C₆H₅	86 87 86	 1 13;26						0.862	4.14	316		2,3
Propyl Benzene—iso	See Cumene											
Propyl Chloride—n C₃H₇Cl	<0	26			2.6	10.5	73	0.890	2.71	115		3
Propyl Chloride—iso (CH₃)₂CHCl	—26	26	1100	26	2.8	10.7	26	0.868	2.71	95		2,3
Propylene C₃H₆ (Propene)	Gas		927 927-952	6	2.0 2.0 2.2 2.0 2.4	11.1 9.0 9.7 11.1 10.3	1 5;12 26 47		1.49	—58		4
Propylene Chlorhydrin CH₃CHOHCH₂Cl	125	12;26						1.113	3.26	261		3
Propylenediamine CH₃CH(NH₂)CH₂NH₂	(o.c.)120	26;83						0.873	2.56	246		3
Propylene Dichloride CH₃CHClCH₂Cl	60 70 59	 12 26	1035	26	3.4	14.5	26	1.15	3.89	205		2,3
Propylene Glycol CH₃CHOHCH₂OH	210	12;26	790	52	2.62	12.55	26	1.040	2.62	370		1,3
Propylene Oxide OCH₂CHCH₃	—35 <—20 —35	128 66			2.1	21.5	26	0.859	2.00	95		3
Propyl Ether—iso (CH₃)₂CHO-CH(CH₃)₂	—18 —18 (o.c.)15	 26 26;83	830 830 781	 26 17				0.73	3.52	156		2,3
Propyl Formate—n HCOOC₃H₇	27	1;13;-26	851	17				0.909	3.03	178		2,3
Propyl Formate—iso HCOOCH(CH₃)₂	22	13;26	905	17				0.873	3.03	153		2,3
Propyl Propionate—n CH₃CH₂COOCH₂-CH₂CH₃	(o.c.)175	26						0.885		245		1,2,3
Pyridine CH<(CHCH)₂>N	68 68 <80 74	22;26 2 28	900 900-1100 1065	28 26	1.8 1.8 1.8	12.5 12.4 12.5	1;26 5	0.982	2.73	239		3
Pyrocatechol C₆H₄(OH)₂	261	13;26						1.344	3.79	474		1,3

	FLASH POINT Deg. F.	Ref.	IGNITION TEMP. Deg. F.	Ref.	EXPLOSIVE LIMITS Per Cent by Volume Low-er	Up-per	Ref.	Sp. Gr. (Water =1)	Vapor Density Air=1	Boiling Point Deg. F.	Und. Lab. Class	Ext. Agt.
Pyroxylin Solution	80 May be below	2										3
Quenching Oil	365	26						0.9				1,2,3
Quinoline C₉H₄N:CHCH:ĊH			896	17				1.095	4.45	460		
Rape Seed Oil (Colza Oil)	325 473 455 325	22 3 26	836	26				0.915				1,2,3
Red Oil	See Oleic Acid											
Resorcinol C₆H₄(OH)₂	261	1;26						1.272	3.79	529		1,3
Rosin Oil	266 266 257	10;26 3	648	26				0.98 0.98-1.1		>680		1,2,3
Rubber Cement	50 or less	2	Note: Hazard depends upon solvent.									1,2,3
Rum (See also Ethyl Alcohol and Water)	77	40										3
Signal Oil	See Mineral Seal Oil											
Sorbic Acid CH₃CH:CHCH:-CHCOOH (2,4—Hexadienoic Acid)	260	129								442 Decom-poses		1
Soy Bean Oil	540 566 540	24 26	833	26				0.925				1,2,3
Sperm Oil No. 1 No. 2	428 460 457	26 3 1;9	586	1								1,2,3
Spindle Oil	See Lubricating Oil											
Stearic Acid CH₃(CH₂)₁₆COOH	385	26	743	26				0.847	9.00	726		1,3
Straw Oil	315-361	42										1,2,3
Styrene C₆H₅CH:CH₂	90	60	914	60	1.1	6.1	69	0.907	3.60	295		2,3
Sulfur	405	26	450	26				2.046		832		1
			Note: See Table of Common Hazardous Chemicals.									
Sulfur Chloride S₂Cl₂	245	26	453	26				1.687	4.66	280		1,3
Tallow	509	26						0.895				1,3
Tallow Oil	492	24:26						0.914				1,3
Tannic Acid (Tannin)	(o.c.)390	26	980	26								1
Tartaric Acid HOOC(CHOH)₂-COOH (Racemic Acid)	(o.c.)410	26	802	26				1.667				1

	FLASH POINT		IGNITION TEMP.		EXPLOSIVE LIMITS Per Cent by Volume			Sp. Gr. (Water =1)	Vapor Density Air=1	Boiling Point Deg. F.	Und. Lab. Class	Ext. Agt.
	Deg. F.	Ref.	Deg. F.	Ref.	Low-er	Up-per	Ref.					
Terphenyl—o $(C_6H_5)_2C_6H_4$	(o.c.)325	26						1.14	7.95	630		1,3
Terphenyl—m $(C_6H_5)_2C_6H_4$	(o.c.)375	26						1.164	7.95	685		1,3
Terphenyl—p $(C_6H_5)_2C_6H_4$	(o.c.)405	26						1.236	7.95	759		1,3
Tetrachlorbenzene $C_6H_2Cl_4$	311	42						1.734	7.4	475		1,3
Tetradecane $CH_3(CH_2)_{12}CH_3$	212	26			0.5		26	0.765	6.83	486		1,2,3
Tetradecanol $C_{14}H_{29}OH$	(o.c.)285	26;83						0.835	7.39	507		1,2,3
Tetraethylene Glycol $HOCH_2(CH_2OCH_2)_3$-CH_2OH	(o.c.)345	26						1.126		621		1,3
Tetraethylene Pentamine $H_2N(C_2H_4NH)_3$-$C_2H_4NH_2$	(o.c.)325	26;83						0.998	6.53	631		1,3
Tetrahydrofuran $OCH_2CH_2CH_2CH_2$ (Tetramethylene Oxide)	(o.c.)<70	130						0.888	2.5	151		
Tetrahydrofurfuryl Alcohol $C_4H_7OCH_2OH$	(o.c.)167 (o.c.)167 176	131						1.064	3.5	352 @743 m.m.		1,3
Tetrahydronaphthalene $C_6H_4(CH_3)_2C_2H_4$ (Tetralin)	171 172 171	1 26						0.973	4.55	403		1,2,3
2,2,3,3—Tetramethyl Pentane $(CH_3)_3CC(CH_3)_2$-CH_2CH_3			806	17								
Thialdine $SCH(CH_3)SCH(CH_3)$-$NHCHCH_3$	(o.c.)200	26;83						1.063	5.63	Decom-poses		1,2,3,
Tin Tetramethyl $Sn(CH_3)_4$					1.90		5;26	1.314		172		2,3
Tin Tetraphenyl $(C_6H_5)_4Sn$	450	42						1.490		795		2,3
Toluene	See Toluol											
Toluidine—o $CH_3C_6H_4NH_2$	185 202 185	28 26	900 900-1000 900	28 26				0.999	3.69	392	20-25	1,2,3
Toluidine—p $CH_3C_6H_4NH_2$	188	26	900	26				0.973	3.90	392		1,2,3
Toluol $C_6H_5CH_3$ (Toluene)	40 46 45 48 40	22 6 28 26	1026 1027 1026 1050-1125 1004	11 26 28 17	1.27 1.3 1.4 1.27 1.4 1.17 0.99 @212°	7.0 6.8 7.0 7.0	11 9 26 4;5 50 50	0.866	3.14	232	75-80	2,3

	FLASH POINT Deg. F.	Ref.	IGNITION TEMP. Deg. F.	Ref.	EXPLOSIVE LIMITS Per Cent by Volume Lower	Upper	Ref.	Sp. Gr. (Water = 1)	Vapor Density Air = 1	Boiling Point Deg. F.	Und. Lab. Class	Ext. Agt.
o—Tolyl p—Toluene Sulfonate $C_{14}H_{14}O_3S$	363	13;26										1,3
Transil Oil (Transformer Oil)	(o.c.)295	26						0.9				1,2,3
Tri-amylamine $(C_5H_{11})_3N$	(o.c.)215	26						0.793	7.83	453		1,2,3
Triamyl Benzene $(C_5H_{11})_3C_6H_3$	(o.c.)270	26						0.87		575		1,2,3
Triamyl Borate $B(C_5H_{11}O)_3$	180	26						0.845		430		1,2,3
Tributylamine $(C_4H_9)_3N$	(o.c.)187	26;94						0.78	6.38	417		1,2,3
Tributyl Citrate $C_3H_4(OH)(COOC_4H_9)_3$	315 315 (o.c.)365	26 26	695	26					12.41	450		1,3
Tributyl Phosphate $(C_4H_9)_3PO_4$	(o.c.)295	26					1	0.973	9.20	560		1,2,3
Trichloro Benzene $C_6H_3Cl_3$	(o.c.)210	26						1.45		415		1,2,3
Trichloro Propane—1,2,3 $CH_2ClCHClCH_2Cl$	165	132						1.385	5.0	313		1,2,3
Trichlorosilane $HSiCl_3$	(o.c.)<20	57						1.34	4.7	89		3
Tri-Cresylphosphate—o $[(C_6H_4)(CH_3)]_3PO_4$ (Tritolyl Phosphate)	460 439 460	13 26	725	133				1.17		770 Decomposes		1,2,3
Triethanolamine $(CH_2OHCH_2)_3N$	355	12;26						1.13	5.14	650		1,3
Triethylamine $(C_2H_5)_3N$	(o.c.)20	26;94						0.73	3.48	193		2,3
Triethylene Glycol $HOCH_2(CH_2OCH_2)_2 CH_2OH$	350 331 360	12 26	700	26	0.89	9.20	26	1.125	5.17	550		1,3
Triethylene Tetramine $H_2NCH_2(CH_2 NHCH_2)_2 CH_2NH_2$	275	26	640	26				0.982		532		1,3
Triglycol Dichloride $ClCH_2(CH_2OCH_2)_2 CH_2Cl$	(o.c.)250	26						1.197		466		1,3
Triisopropanolamine $[(CH_3)_2COH]_3N$	(o.c.)305	26						1.020		570		1,3
Trimethylcyclohexanol $CH(OH)CH_2C(CH_3)_2 CH_2CH(CH_3)CH_2$	(o.c.)165	26;83						0.878	4.91	388		1,2,3
Trimethylhexanol—3,5,5 $CH_3C(CH_3)_2CH_2CH$-$(CH_3)CH_2CH_2OH$	(o.c.)200	134						0.824	5.0	381		1,2,3
Trioxane $OCH_2OCH_2OCH_2$	(o.c.)113	14;26	777	26	3.57	28.7	26			239 Sublimes		2,3

	FLASH POINT Deg. F.	Ref.	IGNITION TEMP. Deg. F.	Ref.	EXPLOSIVE LIMITS Per Cent by Volume Low-er	Up-per	Ref.	Sp. Gr. (Water =1)	Vapor Density Air=1	Boiling Point Deg. F.	Und. Lab. Class	Ext. Agt.
Triphenyl Phosphate (C6H5)3PO4	428	13;26								750		1,3
Tung Oil (China Wood Oil)	552	7;26	855	26;44				0.94				1,3
Turkey Red Oil	476	26;44	833	26;44								1,2,3
Turbine Oil	See Lubricating Oil								.			
Turpentine	95 95 90-95	10;18;- 26 3;16	464 489 464 488 491	25 22 26 50	0.8 0.8 0.69 @212°		26 50	<1		300	40-50	2,3
Ultrasene (Kerosene, Deodorized)	175 175 (o.c.)180	26 26										1,2,3
Undecanol C4H9CH(C2H5)C2H4-CH(OH)CH3	(o.c.)235	26;83						0.836	5.94	437		1,2,3
Varnish	<80	2										2,3
Varnish Shellac	40-70	2;18										3
Varnoline (Safety Solvent)	109	26										2,3
Vegetable Oil, Hydrogenated	(o.c.)610	26						<1				3
Vinyl Acetate CH2CHOOCCH3	18 18 18-23	26 43	800	26						161		2,3
Vinyl Chloride CH2CHCl	(o.c.)<0	26			4	22	5;26	0.97	2.15	7		3
Vinyl Cyclohexene C8H12	61	26	517	26				0.830		266		2,3
Vinyl Ether	See Divinyl Ether								.			
Vinyl Ethyl Ether CH2:CHOC2H5	<—50	26	395	26				0.754	2.5	96		
Vinyl 2—Ethylhexyl Ether CH2:CHOCH2CH-(C2H5)C4H9	116	26	395	26				0.810	5.4			
Vinyl Isopropyl Ether CH2:CHOCH(CH3)2	—26	26	522	26								
Water Gas	See Gas											
Whale Oil	446 446 494	26 9	800	26				0.925				1,2,3
Whiskey	82	40										3
Wines (Sherry and Port) (High)	129 129 60-80	40 2										3

	FLASH POINT		IGNITION TEMP.		EXPLOSIVE LIMITS Per Cent by Volume			Sp. Gr. (Water = 1)	Vapor Density Air= 1	Boiling Point	Und. Lab.	Ext.
	Deg. F.	Ref.	Deg. F.	Ref.	Low- er	Up- per	Ref.			Deg. F.	Class	Agt.
Xylene—o C₆H₄(CH₃)₂ (Xylol—o)	63 86 76 63	6:28 20 26	900 1028 924 900-1150	25 26 28	1.0 1.0 1.2 1.0 1.1	6.0 5.3 6.0 7.0	11 5 26 135	0.88	3.66	291	40-45	2,ა
Xylene—m C₆H₄(CH₃)₂	77	135			1.1	7.0	.̅ 5	0.864	3.66	282		2,3
Xylene—p C₆H₄(CH₃)₂	77	135			1.1	7.0	135	0.861	3.66	281		2,3
Xylidine—o C₆H₃(CH₃)₂NH₂ (Dimethyl Aniline—o)	206 206 207	9:26 6						0.99	4.17	435		1,2,3
Zinc Stearate Zn(C₁₈H₃₅O₂)₂	(o.c.)530	26	790	26								1,2,3

REFERENCES

1. International Critical Tables.
2. Interstate Commerce Commission Regulations, Bureau of Explosives Pamphlet No. 9, 1930.
3. Oil Analysis, II. Gill.
4. Bureau of Mines Technical Paper No. 352.
5. Limits of Inflammability of Gases and Vapors, Bureau of Mines Bulletin No. 279, 1931.
6. Fire and Explosion Risks, Von Schwartz, 1904.
7. Industrial Fire Hazards, Dana-Milne, 1928.
8. Explosives, Arthur Marshall, Vol. 1, 1917.
9. Van Nostrand Chemical Annual, 1922.
10. Condensed Chemical Dictionary, 1930.
11. Solvents, Thos. H. Durrans, 1930.
12. Synthetic Organic Chemicals, Carbide and Carbon Chemicals Corp., 1934.
13. Chemical Markets, Vol. 25, No. 4, Oct. 1929.
14. E. I. du Pont de Nemours & Company.
15. Solvents, Commercial Solvents Corp., 1933.
16. Table of Common Hazardous Chemicals, NFPA, 1950.
17. Bureau of Mines, 1950, (Letter).
18. Bureau of Explosives, Pamphlet No. 7, 1925.
19. Industrial & Engineering Chemistry, Vol. 20, No. 5.
20. Pittsburgh Plate Glass Co., 1931, (Letter).
21. Standard Oil Development Co., 1931, (Letter).
22. Underwriters' Laboratories, Inc. Report SI528 on Propagation of Flame in Pipes and Effectiveness of Arresters, 1919.
24. Fire and Explosion Hazards of Commercial Oils, William Vlachos and C. A. Vlachos, 1921.
25. Industrial & Engineering Chemistry, Vol. 21, No. 2, P. 134.
26. Factory Mutuals—Properties of Flammable Liquids, Gases and Solids—May, 1950.
27. Underwriters' Laboratories, Inc. Report MH1130 on the Fire Hazards of Ethane, Propane, Butane, and Ammonia as Refrigerants, 1923.
28. Underwriters' Laboratories, Inc. Method for the Classification of the Hazards of Liquids, 1929.
29. Underwriters' Laboratories, Inc. Report MH2066 on Fumigants, Ethylene Oxide and Carboxide, 1930.

30. Research Work on the Explosive Range of Illuminating Gas, Underwriters' Laboratories (a supplement to Reference No. 22).
31. Fuels and Their Combustion, Haslam and Russell, 1926.
33. Zeitschrift Für Elektrochemie, 1923.
34. Chemical Abstracts, 1928.
35. Industrial & Engineering Chemistry, June, 1933.
36. Bureau of Mines, R. I., 3794.
37. Industrial & Engineering Chemistry, May, 1930, p. 513.
38. Underwriters' Laboratories, Inc. List of Inspected Gas, Oil and Miscellaneous Appliances, Jan., 1940.
39. Underwriters' Laboratories, Inc. Report MH2375 on the Comparative Life, Fire and Explosion Hazards of Common Refrigerants, 1933.
40. Fire Prevention and Protection, The Spectator Company, 1916.
41. Extraction of Gasoline from Natural Gas by Absorption Methods, Bureau of Mines Bulletin No. 120, 1917.
42. Hooker Electrochemical Co., Bul. 100, 1947-1948.
43. Solvent News, U. S. Industrial Chemicals, Inc., June, 1934.
44. Trans. Electro Chemical Society, 1933, page 443.
46. Underwriters Laboratories, Inc. Card Data Service.
47. Bureau of Mines, R. I., 3395.
48. Bureau of Mines, R. I., 3669.
49. Bureau of Mines, R. I., 3565.
50. Underwriters' Laboratories, Inc. Bulletin of Research No. 43.
51. Shell Chemical Corp., Chem. & Eng. News (Advt.) 27:22, May 30, 1949.
52. Bureau of Mines, R. I., 4502.
53. Commercial Solvents Corp., Chem. & Eng. News (Advt.) 28:8, Feb. 20, 1950.
54. Hooker Electrochemical Co., Prelim. Tech. Data Sheet No. 350-A.
55. Dow Chemical Co., Chem. & Eng. News (Advt.) 27:50, Dec. 12, 1949.
56. Monsanto Chemical Co., Monsanto Plasticizers, 1949.
57. Plaskon Co., Inc.
58. Underwriters Laboratories Card Data Service, Serial No. 26, July, 1949.
59. Hooker Electrochemical Co., Prelim. Tech. Data Sheet No. 363, May, 1948.
60. Petrov, Bulletin Acad. Sci. (USSR) Chem. Sect. (1941) 4-5, pages 533-543.
61. Hooker Electrochemical Co., Tech. Data Sheet 369, March, 1949.
62. Sharples Chemicals, Inc., Chem. & Eng. News (Advt.) 28:23, June 5, 1950.
63. Carbide and Carbon Chemicals Corp., Tech. Inf. Sheet F-6934, Sept., 1947.
64. Petrov and Andrew, J. Gen. Chem. (USSR), Vol. 12, pages 95-8 (1942).
65. Commercial Solvents Corp., Chem. & Eng. News (Advt.) 27:40, Oct. 3, 1949.
66. Chemicals Available in Research Quantities—Carbide and Carbon Chemicals Corporation.
67. Bureau of Mines, R. I., 3727—Oct., 1943.
68. Underwriters Laboratories Card Data Service, Serial No. UL-427, April, 1944.
69. Bureau of Mines, R. I., 3630.
70. Chemical Dictionary, 3d Edition.
71. Bureau of Mines, R. I., 3602.
72. Bureau of Mines, R. I., 3648.
73. Bureau of Mines, R. I., 3490.
74. Bureau of Mines, R. I., 3537.
75. Allied Chemical & Dye Corp., Indus. & Eng. Chem., March 16, 1943.
76. Commercial Solvents Corp., Catalog, Jan. 20, 1942.
77. Lange's Handbook of Chemistry, 5th Ed., 1944.
78. Physical Constants of the Principal Hydrocarbons, The Texas Co., 1939.
79. Sharples Chemicals Co., Indus. & Eng. Chem., March 16, 1943.

80. Bureau of Mines, R. I., 3443.
81. Bureau of Mines, R. I., 3454.
82. Bureau of Mines, R. I., 3640.
83. Physical Properties of Synthetic Organic Chemicals, Carbide and Carbon Chemicals Corp.
84. Factory Mutual Laboratories, 1947.
85. Becco Sales Corporation, October 10, 1944.
86. Solvents and Chemicals, U. S. Industrial Chemicals, Inc., 1942 Edition.
87. Sharples Chemicals, Inc., Synthetic Organic Chemicals, 1946.
88. Chemical Safety Data Sheets, Manufacturing Chemists' Assn.
89. Phillips Hydrocarbons, 1946 Edition.
90. Bureau of Mines, R. I., 3597.
91. Union Bay State Co., Data Sheet, 1945.
92. Fire and Explosion Hazards of the Manufacture of Synthetic Rubber, NBFU Research Report No. 4.
93. Engineer Research and Development Laboratories, U. S. Army, Report 1177, Aug. 18, 1950.
94. Sharples Chemicals, Inc., Synthetic Organic Chemicals, 1942.
95. E. I. du Pont de Nemours & Co., Chem. & Eng. News (Advt.) 27:13, March 28, 1949.
96. Arapahoe Chemicals, Inc., Chem. & Eng. News (Advt.) 27:9, Feb. 28, 1949.
97. Celanese Corp. of America, Bul. S-08-1.
98. Sharples Chemicals, Inc., Chem. & Eng. News (Advt.) 26:44, Nov. 1, 1948.
99. General Aniline & Film Corp., Chem. & Eng. News (Advt.) 27:6, Feb. 7, 1949.
100. Shell Chemical Corp., Chem. Eng. (Advt.) 55:4, April, 1948.
101. Dow Chemical Co., Ind. & Eng. Chem. (Advt.) 42:8, Aug. 1950.
102. Carbide and Carbon Chemicals Corp., The Physical Properties of Synthetic Chemicals, 1950.
103. Explosion Hazards, W. N. Vlachos, 1941.
104. Carbide and Carbon Chemicals Corp., Organic Nitrogen Compounds.
105. Dow Chemical Co., Chem. & Eng. News (Advt.) 28:1, Jan. 2, 1950.
106. American Chemical Society, Monograph No. 98.
107. Bureau of Mines, R. I., 3284.
108. Bureau of Standards, Commercial Standard CS12-48.
109. Underwriters Laboratories Card Data Service, Serial No. 431, May, 1944.
111. Dow Chemical Co., Chem. & Eng. News (Advt.) 28:3, Jan. 16, 1950.
112. Factory Mutuals, Properties of Flammable Liquids, Gases and Solids, Jan., 1945.
113. Shell Chemical Corp., Chem. & Eng. News (Advt.) 26:18, May 3, 1948.
114. Shell Chemical Corp., Tech. Pub. S. C. 48-1.
115. Shell Chemical Corp., Organic Chemicals, 2d Edition 1942.
116. Commercial Solvents Corp., Chem. & Eng. News (Advt.) 27:28, July 11, 1949.
117. Bureau of Mines, R. I., 4125.
118. E. I. du Pont de Nemours & Co., Chem. Ab. (Advt.) 42:8, April 20, 1948.
119. Shell Chemical Corp., Chem. & Eng. News (Advt.) 25152, Dec. 29, 1947.
120. Celanese Corp. of America, Ind. & Eng. Chem. (Advt.) 39:9, Sept., 1947.
121. Underwriters Laboratories Card Data Service, Serial No. 424, March, 1944.
122. Underwriters Laboratories Card Data Service, Serial No. 195, Dec., 1939.
123. Townsend, D. T. A. and MacCormac, M., J. Inst. Petroleum, 25, 1939.
124. E. I. du Pont de Nemours & Co., Chem. & Eng. News (Advt.) 25:38, Sept. 22, 1947.
125. Dow Chemical Co., Chem. & Eng. News (Advt.) 27:52, Dec. 26, 1949.
126. Bureau of Mines, R. I., 4671.
127. Celanese Corp. of America, SPECIF Bul. S-09-1.

98   SAFETY IN THE CHEMICAL LABORATORY

128. Dow Chemical Co., Chem. & Eng. News (Advt.) 27:48, Nov. 28, 1949.
129. Carbide and Carbon Chemicals Corp., Organic Acids, June, 1948.
130. Celanese Corp. of America, Ind. & Eng. Chem. (Advt.) 39:4, April, 1947.
131. Quaker Oats Co., Ind. & Eng. Chem. (Advt.) 39:12, Dec., 1947.
132. Shell Chemical Corp., Chem. & Eng. News (Advt.) 26:29, July 19, 1948.
133. Underwriters Laboratories Card Data Service, Serial No. 452, Jan. 1946.
134. E. I. du Pont de Nemours & Co., Chem. Eng. (Advt.) 57:9, Sept., 1950.
135. American Standards Association, Xylene, Allowable Concentrations of, Z37.10—
    1948.

Dusts

Another fire hazard is posed by dusts.[7] Practically all organic substances (and some that are commonly considered noncombustible), if in finely divided form and mixed with air in the proper proportions, can be ignited to cause violent explosions. The U. S. Department of Agriculture lists 133 dusts according to their degree of explosiveness.

Following are the most common types found to be explosive:

Type of Dust	Example
Carbon	Coal, peat, charcoal, coke
Fertilizers	Bone meal, fish meal, blood flour
Food products and by-products	Starches, sugars, flour, cocoa, powdered milk, grain dust
Metal powders	Aluminum, magnesium, zinc, iron
Resins, waxes and soaps	Shellac, resin, gum sodium resinate
Spices, drugs and insecticides	Cinnamon, pepper, gentian, pyrethrum
Wood, paper, tanning materials	Wood flour, wood dust, cellulose, cork, bark dust, wood extract
Miscellaneous	Chemical products, hard rubber, sulfur and tobacco

For further particulars, see Chapter VIII on Toxicity.

Preventing Dust Explosions. There are three ways to avoid dust explosions:

1. Prevent formation of explosive mixtures of dust and air.
2. Prevent ignition of such mixtures if their formation cannot be entirely prevented.

[7] The material on dusts is based on the discussion of this subject in the *Accident Prevention Manual for Industrial Operations* of the National Safety Council.

3. Maintain the operation under an inert gas.

Frequent cleaning and extensive use of local exhaust will help to minimize the dust explosion hazard. Where possible, dusty operations should be segregated and dust-producing equipment should be totally enclosed and exhausted to prevent leakage of dust into the general working area. Large-size dust handling equipment must be provided with explosion vents, if the dust handled is combustible (see National Fire Codes, Vol. II, Prevention of Dust Explosions).

CHAPTER VII

Chemical Hazards

This chapter discusses the hazards associated with some of the more widely used chemicals found in the laboratory. Those selected are for illustrative purposes only. For more complete information on their properties, hazards, and safeguards against exposure, reference is made frequently to respective MCA Chemical Safety Data Sheets, listed under "Literature References."

Chemical hazards are discussed under three sections—namely, Acids and Alkalies, Oxidizing Materials, and Explosive Power.

By the term "chemical hazards" in this publication is meant the fire, health, and handling hazards which arise from the handling and storage of the chemicals and materials most frequently used in the chemical laboratory. These hazards may lead to personal injury (1) through contact with the skin or mucous membranes, including inhalation, (2) through ingestion, and (3) because of danger to health and life as well as damage to property through fires or explosions. Accordingly, the hazards of each chemical should be known and the particular safe handling methods practiced (for Clothing and Personal Protective Equipment, see Chapter XI).

ACIDS AND ALKALIES

Some of the most hazardous chemicals, falling within this category, are the so-called "strong" or "mineral" acids, such as hydrochloric, hydrofluoric, sulfuric, and nitric. The organic acids as a class, characterized by the presence of a COOH group, are much less hazardous because of their comparatively low ionization potentials, and because few, if any, of them "fume." Phenol (commonly called carbolic acid), although not a strong organic acid, is a very toxic chemical by contact with the skin, oral intake, or inhalation of its vapors. Hydrocyanic and oxalic acids, likewise, are extremely hazardous compounds, not because of their acidic properties, but because of their toxicity.

Perchloric acid is a very hazardous chemical, because of its corrosive nature and its strong oxidizing and explosive properties. It is referred to later in this chapter under the heading, "Oxidizing Materials."

It would be impractical to arrange a list of the strong organic or mineral acids used in the laboratory strictly in the order of their degree of hazard. On the other hand, several of these acids rank as the most hazardous products commonly used in the chemical laboratory. These acids, therefore, are placed in Class A, the others of the strong mineral acids in Class B, and the organic acids in Class C.

Class A Acids	Class B Acids	Class C Acids
Hydrofluoric	Hydrochloric	Formic
Sulfuric	Phosphoric	Acetic
Chlorosulfonic		
Nitric		
Chromic		

Acids having a relatively lower degree of handling hazard include maleic, succinic, benzoic, and oxalic. In this chapter only a few are described in relation to the hazards involved.

Hydrofluoric Acid (Class A)

Hydrofluoric acid is used in both anhydrous and aqueous forms. At atmospheric pressure the anhydrous acid is a liquid when kept at 19.4°C or below. Above this temperature, and at atmospheric pressure, it vaporizes. Aqueous hydrofluoric acid at normal temperatures and atmospheric pressure is a liquid; however, vapors are emitted from the aqueous acid which can vary in strength from very dilute to 80% HF. Both the liquid and vapor forms of hydrofluoric acid are extremely dangerous when in contact with any part of the body. The vapor form is extremely irritating to the respiratory tract and can cause death through the development of pulmonary edema.

The generally accepted maximum concentration of hydrofluoric acid vapor is 3 ppm by volume in air for an 8-hour working day. Concentrations of 50 ppm or more may be fatal in 30 to 60 minutes.

Eyes

Contact of liquid or vapor with the eyes immediately causes severe irritation of the eyes or eyelids. If the hydrofluoric acid is not rapidly removed by thorough irrigation with water, there may be prolonged or permanent visual defects, or even total destruction of the eyesight.

Skin

Either the anhydrous or aqueous acid can cause severe burns to the skin. These may differ widely depending upon the concentration of the acid. When the contact is with an acid concentration of 20% or less, the burns do not usually manifest themselves until several hours have elapsed. Concentrations of from 21% to 60% are usually detected much earlier. Concentrations of from 61% to 100% usually are felt immediately.

Fingernails

Contacts of hydrofluoric acid with areas around the fingernails are extremely painful. Unless promptly attended to they can lead to infiltration of the acid into the deeper structures with the resulting destruction of tissues or even the bone. Eventually such infiltration may necessitate amputation.

Inhalation

Hydrofluoric acid vapor is extremely irritating to all parts of the respiratory tract. Severe exposures will lead rapidly to inflammation and congestion of the lungs, and the latter may be fatal within a short time if proper medical attention is not promptly administered.

Oral Intake

When swallowed, hydrofluoric acid will immediately cause severe irritation of, and damage to, the mouth, esophagus, and stomach. Severe damage to the respiratory tract will also occur.

Chronic Toxicity

As far as is now known, chronic poisoning by hydrofluoric acid has not been recorded.

Injury Prevention

The most important factors in the prevention of hydrofluoric acid injury are:

1. Keep the concentration of vapor in the atmosphere below 3 ppm by volume.
2. Prevent all contact of vapor or liquid with any part of the body.
3. Secure prompt first aid and medical attention in case of any kind of body contact with the acid.

(See Manual Sheet SD-25, Hydrofluoric Acid.)

Sulfuric Acid (Class A)

Sulfuric acid is one of the most common of the chemicals used in the laboratory. It is employed in strengths varying from very dilute to 100% acid, and above this in the form of "fuming acid" or oleum, which results from dissolving sulfur trioxide, the anhydride of sulfuric acid, in 100% acid. A mixture of 20% sulfur trioxide and 80% sulfuric acid is known as 20% oleum; the 35% mixture as 35% oleum, etc. Sulfuric acid is dangerous when improperly handled, the degree of hazard being approximately proportional to the concentration of the acid. Dilute solutions, up to 5% strength, may be handled readily, except for the danger of splashes into the eyes; in cases of body contact the acid can be washed off readily with water.

Eyes

Contact of any concentration of sulfuric acid with the eyes is dangerous. The higher concentrations, 65% or above, are particularly hazardous. These can cause rapid and severe damage which may be followed by total loss of sight.

Skin

Concentrated solutions of sulfuric acid are rapidly destructive to body tissues, producing severe burns. Repeated and unattended contacts with dilute acid may cause dermatitis.

Inhalation

Inhalation of vapor from hot sulfuric acid or from oleum at any temperature may cause a rapid loss of consciousness with serious damage to the lung tissue. Individual sensitivity to such vapor is variable; 0.125 to 0.50 ppm of vapor in air may be mildly annoying; 1.5 to 2.5 ppm definitely unpleasant, and 10 to 20 ppm unbearable. Workers exposed to low concentrations of vapor gradually lose the sensitivity to the irritant action and are therefore prone to take risks. Utmost alertness must be exercised.

Oral Intake

The degree of danger in this respect is approximately proportional to the strength of the acid swallowed. Concentrated acid may cause severe damage to the mouth, esophagus, or stomach, or even death.

Injury Prevention

Some of the important measures for the prevention of injury by sulfuric acid are:

1. Keep the concentration of vapors of the acid below 0.25 ppm, by volume in air.
2. Prevent all contact of the vapor or the higher concentration of the acid with any part of the body.

3. Wash off thoroughly with water all acid which may have contacted any part of the body.

4. Obtain prompt first aid and medical treatment in case of any kind of body contact with concentrations of the acid in strengths of 50% or above.

(See Manual Sheet SD-20, Sulfuric Acid.)

Chlorosulfonic Acid (Class A)

Inasmuch as chlorosulfonic acid is the product obtained by combining one molecule of sulfur trioxide (SO_3) with one molecule of hydrogen chloride (HCl), and since the material breaks down with moisture or water to form sulfuric and hydrochloric acids, it has only one strength, represented by the formula $SO_2(OH)Cl$.

Chlorosulfonic acid is a clear to cloudy, colorless to pale yellow liquid boiling at 151-152°C (Merck's Index, 1952) at 755 mm pressure. It is highly corrosive and dangerously reactive. In addition to attacking most metals, it is a strong oxidizing agent and will react with water or organic materials with the evolution of heat and large quantities of dense white fumes.

'Either the liquid acid or its vapor is dangerous when in contact with body tissues. The vapor has such a sharp and penetrating odor that inhalation of toxic quantities is unlikely, unless the person exposed is trapped in such a location as would make escape from the vapor impossible. (The maximum allowable concentration of hydrochloric acid, even when derived from the breakdown of chlorosulfonic acid, is 10 ppm.)

Chlorosulfonic acid acts upon most metals with the evolution of hydrogen, which is flammable and explosive when mixed with air.

The greatest hazard in handling chlorosulfonic acid is the danger of eye or skin contact. It is fully as hazardous in these respects as fuming sulfuric acid, and as dangerous as hydrochloric acid.

Nitric Acid (Class A)

Just as in the case of sulfuric acid, the degree of hazard existing in handling nitric acid is approximately proportional to the concentration of the acid, which may vary from very dilute to "fuming." Strengths above 85% are considered fuming acid, and "red fuming acid" is high strength nitric acid containing varying percentages of oxides of nitrogen in solution at normal temperatures. At elevated temperatures all nitric acids give off gaseous oxides of nitrogen. These "nitrous fumes" are extremely toxic. The color of these fumes varies from colorless through shades of yellow and red to dark brown, depending upon the nature of the oxides present and density of the fumes. In addition, the stronger nitric acids are extremely damaging to body tissues, and particularly to the eyes.

Eyes

Severe and permanent damage to the eyes, with possible loss of eyesight, will result from failure to treat promptly all contacts of the acid with the eyes. Symptoms of burning and eye watering demand immediate treatment.

Skin

The first symptoms of strong nitric acid contacts with skin are smarting, itching, and yellow discoloration. If the acid is not removed at once, intense pain and severe burns result. Chronic ulceration may follow with subsequent permanent scarring. Dilute solutions of nitric acid may cause chronic skin irritation.

Inhalation

Nitric acid vapors or the fumes from nitric acid (nitrous fumes) are highly toxic, being capable of producing severe injury or even death. The extremely toxic oxides of nitrogen are formed whenever nitric acid comes in contact with certain heavy metals, or with organic materials, such as wood, cloth, or paper. The toxic effects are seldom due to nitric acid vapors alone or to a single one of the gaseous oxides of nitrogen, but usually result from a mixture of the toxic compounds.

Since each one of these compounds when acting alone is capable of producing definite effects, which vary with the composition of the chemical compound, the signs and symptoms of toxicity vary in character and severity according to the composition of the noxious mixture.

The gaseous oxides of nitrogen consist of nitrous oxide (N_2O), nitric oxide (NO), nitrogen dioxide (NO_2), nitrogen trioxide (N_2O_3), and nitrogen peroxide or nitrogen tetroxide (N_2O_4). The most dangerous are the two forms of nitrogen oxides—N_2O_4 which is a colorless, or yellow liquid, and NO_2 which is reddish or dark brown; both are highly toxic. *Therefore, the intensity of color is not an indicator of the degree of danger*— the gas may be a mixture.

The oxides of nitrogen are among the most treacherous of the noxious gases because of the insidious onset of severe, and sometimes fatal, lung congestion (pulmonary edema). The breathing throughout an 8-hour period of as little as 25 ppm may cause signs of pulmonary edema, after a virtually asymptomatic interval of from 5 to as many as 48 hours. Delayed pulmonary edema may follow exposure to higher concentrations for only 1 hour, while a few breaths of the gaseous oxides in a concentration of 200 to 700 ppm will produce severe pulmonary damage, which may result in fatal lung congestion after 5 to 8 hours have elapsed.

Experience has indicated that the typical sequence of events in poisoning by gaseous oxides of nitrogen is: (1) a few "whiffs" of the seemingly innocuous gas; (2) no immediate reaction or very slight respiratory difficulty, headache, dizziness or lassitude (occasionally nausea and vomiting may occur immediately after exposure, or a noisy, asthmatic type of breathing may appear which usually disappears within a half hour), the victim usually persisting in his work; (3) 5 to 8 hours after the exposure, perhaps after the worker has returned home, another person notices that the patient's lips or ears have become cyanotic (blue); (4) there follows rapidly increasing difficulty in breathing with accelerated, somewhat irregular, respiration and choking, dizziness, headache, increasing blueness of the lips or ears which is a sign of severe cyanosis, a sensation of tightness in the chest and anxiety resulting from oxygen hunger; occasionally there are also nausea and vomiting, lassitude, and palpitation. Untreated cases frequently terminate fatally as a result of severe pulmonary congestion, i.e., from suffocation. Physical examination within a short time after the exposure reveals an accelerated respiratory rate, decreased vital capacity, generally suppressed breath sound with occasional moist rales and rhonchi, low blood pressure, and an elevated blood count (10-100% above normal), all of which become more pronounced in inadequately treated cases as time passes.

Before pulmonary edema actually develops, there may be an abnormally low systolic, diastolic, and pulse pressure. After pulmonary edema develops, the pulse pressure rises greatly and may exceed 50 to 60 mm of mercury.

It is most important to realize that prompt, efficient treatment during the quiescent or asymptomatic stage may avert completely the delayed, serious, and sometimes fatal, sequelae of pulmonary injury caused by inhalation of gaseous oxides.

Oral Intake

Taking nitric acid by mouth results in the corrosion of those tissues of the gastro-intestinal tract with which it comes in contact. There is a yellow discoloration of the oral mucosa and severe swelling of the mucous membranes of the throat which may interfere seriously with swallowing and breathing. Strong acid not removed promptly from the stomach may corrode the gastric mucosa so extensively as to result in a perforation of the stomach wall and cause death. In these cases there is some pain, nausea, and vomiting of "coffee grounds" material. (See Manual Sheet SD-5, Nitric Acid.)

Chromic Acids (Class A)

The true chromic acids do not exist as such. They are not encountered in the chemical laboratory. What is commonly used, however, and termed "chromic acid," is a solution of chromium trioxide, CrO_3, in concentrated sulfuric acid. The solution, prepared by treating a chromate or a dichromate with concentrated sulfuric acid, is used generally as a "cleaning solution" for glassware or porcelain ware laboratory apparatus.

Naturally a solution of this kind embodies all the hazard associated with concentrated sulfuric acid itself. In addition, it is a very strong oxidizing agent, and it is upon this property that its cleansing action depends. It follows, therefore, that "chromic acid" is somewhat more corrosive to body tissues than strong sulfuric acid.

Chromic Acid (Chromium Trioxide)

In the use of chromium trioxide, whether this involves handling in the laboratory or in the industry, some of the important properties should be well understood. These are:

1. Chromic acid, as a strong oxidizing agent, attacks most common metals, particularly at elevated temperatures.

2. It attacks cloth fibers, leather, and certain, but not all, synthetic plastics.

3. It reacts rapidly with organic compounds which, if not controlled, may assume violent proportions.

4. It can destroy animal tissues, causing severe burns.

5. It irritates the mucous membrane and the skin.

6. It may ignite oxidizable substances.

7. Contact with the eyes may result in loss of sight.

8. It may irritate the respiratory system when inhaled in dust form.

9. It can act as its own emetic or purgative; if retained in the stomach and kidneys, complications may ensue.

(See Manual Sheet SD-44, Chromic Acid.)

Ammonium, Potassium, and Sodium Dichromates

Ammonium, potassium, and sodium dichromates in solution exhibit properties similar to chromic acid. Accordingly, most of the hazards involved can be avoided by carefully observing the precautions listed in relation to chromium trioxide. A more complete discussion of these compounds will be found in this chapter under the heading of "Oxidizing Materials."

Hydrochloric Acid (Class B)

This is perhaps the most extensively employed acid in the chemical laboratory. It is a solution of hydrogen chloride in water. In strength it generally varies from extremely dilute to approximately 31%, although acid as strong as 37%, the "fuming acid," can be obtained readily. When a concentrated solution is heated, hydrochloric acid gas is given off, but if a dilute solution is heated water is given off. In either case, when the composition of the liquid is that represented by the formula $HCl \cdot 8H_2O$, a constant boiling (20.24%) mixture distills unchanged at ordinary pressures.

Some of the important features, to be observed in the handling of hydrochloric acid (aqueous) and hydrogen chloride gas, may be summarized thus:

1. Avoid contact with metals which are likely to be corroded by hydrochloric acid or hydrogen chloride gas.

2. Avoidance of breathing vapors is essential. Contact with skin and eyes can lead to serious injuries.

3. Observe strict regulations with respect to labeling of containers and bottles.

4. Education and enforced use of personal protective equipment with respect to goggles, face shields, respiratory apparatus, headgear, and masks should be emphasized.

5. Hydrogen chloride gas should always be handled in closed systems.

Hydrochloric acid solutions are not nearly as hazardous by body contact as are the Class A acids. Yet dilute as well as strong acid, if kept in contact with body tissues, can cause severe acid burns. Such cases may arise through the wearing of gloves or shoes wet with hydrochloric acid solution.

Inhalation of appreciable quantities of hydrochloric acid gas may cause damage to the respiratory tract and even lead to the development of pulmonary edema. (See Manual Sheet SD-39, Hydrochloric Acid.)

Phosphoric Acid (Class B)

Of the various acids derived from phosphorus, two are of importance: phosphorous acid (H_3PO_3), and phosphoric acid (H_3PO_4). Only the latter is commonly used in the laboratory. It varies from extremely dilute to 85% strength, the so-called "syrupy" phosphoric acid.

Dilute solutions of phosphoric acid are quite harmless, in fact they are usually dispensed at soda fountains for beverage use. But as with sulfuric and nitric acids, the hazards in handling it increase in approximate proportion to the strength of the acid. Strong phosphoric acid, i.e., above 50% strength, can cause serious burns of body tissue, particularly of the eyes. The degree of hazard also increases with the temperature of the acid. Hot concentrated phosphoric acid is capable of producing severe body burns. (See Manual Sheet SD-28, Phosphoric Anhydride.)

Formic Acid (Class C)

Formic acid is a colorless liquid with a boiling point of 100.8°C. It is miscible with water in all proportions, and consequently any strength of acid may be found in the chemical laboratory.

The degree of hazard which exists in handling formic acid varies with its strength and temperature. The 100% acid, when in contact with body tissues, causes extreme pain and serious burns. Dilute acid, from 5% upward, can also cause injury through prolonged contact; such vapors, particularly from the hot acid, are extremely irritating to the eyes, nasal passages, and the respiratory tract.

Acetic Acid (Class C)

Acetic acid is a colorless liquid, having a boiling point of 118.1°C (minimum grade of "glacial," 99.5%). It is miscible with water in all proportions, and therefore any strength may be found. Glacial acetic acid will ignite, particularly at elevated temperatures.

The degree of hazard which exists in handling acetic acid varies with its strength and temperature. The glacial grade must be stored at a temperature above 20°C in order to prevent freezing and breaking of glass containers.

Concentrated solutions of acetic acid can destroy human tissues with which they may come in contact, and thus produce severe burns. It can cause severe eye damage. Breathing of concentrated vapor may be harmful.

Because of highly corrosive properties of acetic acid, particularly in dilute form, it is important that the personnel handling it be protected against all exposures to its vapors and liquid forms. (See Manual Sheet SD-41, Acetic Acid.)

Boric Acid, Maleic Acid, Succinic Acid, and Benzoic Acid (Class C)

These acids comprise examples of a class of weak acids that are mildly toxic if ingested in any considerable quantity. General precautions with respect to toxicity should be carefully observed.

Alkalies

As in the case of acids, there are "strong" and "weak" alkalies. Their properties are dependent upon their ionization potentials in aqueous solutions. Whereas the acids dissociate to form hydrogen ions (H), the alkalies dissociate to give hydroxyl (OH) ions. These properties give the alkalies their "basic" and "caustic" characteristics.

Four of the alkalies commonly used in the chemical laboratory are:

Strong Alkalies:	Sodium Hydroxide (Caustic Soda)
	Potassium Hydroxide (Caustic Potash)
Weak Alkalies:	Calcium Hydroxide (Lime and Water)
	Ammonium Hydroxide (Aqua Ammonia)

"Strong" alkalies are hazardous substances and should be handled with the greatest of care, whether solid or in solution.

Sodium Hydroxide (Caustic Soda, Lye)

Sodium hydroxide (NaOH) is handled in both liquid and solid forms. The liquid form, known as "liquid caustic," may vary in strength from extremely dilute to about 73% solution, whereas the solid material may occur as bulk, flaked, ground, powdered, or stick forms. The last named (the C.P. grade) is frequently used in the chemical laboratory.

Sodium hydroxide is a white solid that dissolves readily in water, with the evolution of much heat, to a colorless solution. The solid material melts at 310° to 320°C (590°F), depending upon the purity of the material. A 50% solution boils at 142° to 148°C (288° to 298°F), and the 73% solution boils at 188° to 198°C (370° to 388°F). Both the solid and solution forms are very corrosive and dangerously reactive.

Sodium hydroxide is extremely hazardous in contact with the skin, eyes, or mucous membranes, or by oral intake. The solid material can cause severe "caustic burns." Even dilute solutions are dangerous through contact with the eyes, and minute quantities of the solid may cause severe eye injuries. The molten solid is perhaps the most dangerous form, capable of producing blindness, even when the speediest medical treatment is applied. Inhalation of the dust of powdered sodium hydroxide is capable of producing severe damage to the respiratory tract. Solid or liquid caustic soda, when swallowed, will produce severe injury to the mouth, tongue, esophagus, and stomach lining. (See Manual Sheet SD-9, Caustic Soda.)

Potassium Hydroxide

Potassium hydroxide (KOH), like sodium hydroxide, is handled in both liquid and solid forms. The liquid form (liquid caustic potash) may vary in strength from an extremely dilute to a 48-50% solution; and the solid material may occur as bulk, flaked, ground, granular, or stick forms, the last named (the C.P. grade) being commonly used in the chemical laboratory.

Potassium hydroxide is a white solid which dissolves readily in water to a colorless solution, with the evolution of much heat.

The solid material melts over a wide range of temperatures, depending upon its water content; for example, the 85% grade melts at about 125° C (257°F), and the 90% grade melts at about 285°C (545°F). Both the solid and solution forms are very corrosive and dangerously reactive.

Potassium hydroxide is hazardous when in contact with the skin, eyes, or mucous membranes, or by oral intake. The solid material can cause severe "caustic burns." Even dilute solutions are dangerous through contact with the eyes, and minute quantities of the solid material may cause severe eye injury. As in the case of sodium hydroxide, the molten solid is perhaps the most dangerous form of potassium hydroxide.

It is capable of producing blindness even when the speediest medical treatment is applied. Inhalation of the dust of powdered potassium hydroxide is capable of producing severe damage to the respiratory tract. Solid or liquid caustic potash, when swallowed, will produce severe damage to the mouth, tongue, esophagus, and stomach lining. (See Manual Sheet SD-10, Caustic Potash.)

Calcium Hydroxide (Lime)

Calcium hydroxide results from the reaction of water with calcium oxide (CaO), or "burnt lime." At 580°C (1076°F), it loses a molecule of water and reverts to calcium oxide (CaO). The hydroxide itself is sparingly soluble in water, 0.17 parts in 100 parts of water at 0°C (32°F) and 0.08 parts at 100°C (212°F); yet, a suspension of $Ca(OH)_2$ in water (milk of lime) is strongly alkaline. This suspension is capable of producing severe eye injury, and long or continuous exposure may result in damage to the skin. Therefore, gloves, shoes, or clothing wet with limewater should not be worn.

Portland cement containing uncombined or loosely bound CaO, when mixed with water, is strongly alkaline due to its content of calcium hydroxide. Mortar is a combination of sand and calcium hydroxide. For this reason, skin or eye contact with "cement mud" or mortar is to be avoided.

Ammonium Hydroxide

Ammonium hydroxide, or "aqua ammonia," results upon dissolving anhydrous ammonia (NH_3) in water. Such a solution may vary in strength from infinitely dilute to about 29% ammonia at ordinary temperatures. Weak solutions are commonly found in the home as "household ammonia."

In spite of the fact that weak solutions of ammonia are commonly used, such solutions are hazardous in three ways; first, by the inhalation of gaseous ammonia; second, by eye or skin contact; and third, by oral intake. The degree of danger in each case is proportional to the strength of the ammonium hydroxide solution.

Some of the principal hazards in handling anhydrous ammonia gas are:

1. Anhydrous ammonia is a strongly irritating chemical to the skin, mucous membrane, respiratory tract, and eyes. Direct exposure by contact can cause severe burns.

2. Although fire and explosion hazards are not great, the gas is flammable in high concentration, particularly in presence of combustible materials, or oxygen and oil. When thus confined, explosions may follow, particularly at elevated temperatures and high pressures.

3. It is corrosive when in contact with copper and copper containing alloys, if moisture is present.

(See Manual Sheets SD-8, Anhydrous Ammonia and SD-13, Aqua Ammonia.)

Oxidizing Materials

Such oxidizing agents as chlorates, peroxides, perchlorates, and perchloric acid, in contact with organic matter, can cause explosions and fire. They are exothermic and decompose rapidly, liberating oxygen which reacts with the organic compounds.

The following discussion includes several typical products of this type, but many other examples could be cited to illustrate the precautionary principles to be applied in handling such materials.

Chlorine Dioxide

Chlorine dioxide is a bleaching agent, derived from sodium chlorite and chlorine. It is a powerful oxidizing agent, approximately two and one-half times as strong in this respect as chlorine. It is capable of forming explosive mixtures with air, readily set off by exposure to heat, electrostatic discharges, or even sunlight. In the presence of organic matter it can react violently and, if not properly controlled, can be hazardous.

Chlorates

Among the chlorates, sodium chlorate is illustrative of a class which presents a variety of hazards, such as fire and explosions. By itself it is a relatively stable chemical and lends itself to safe handling if the worker:

1. Knows its chemical and physical properties.

2. Knows its reactions with strong acids; it can generate toxic chlorine dioxide and may even cause explosions, since the reaction is exothermic.

3. Keeps it out of contact (except under controlled conditions) with substances such as—

sulfur	ammonium compounds
sulfides	powdered metals
phosphorus	oils and greases
sugars	sawdust (wood dust)
alcohols	lint
solvents	vegetable dusts

All of the above, and many other organic bodies, can cause fires or explosions when in intimate contact with the chemical.

4. Keeps dry chlorate-contaminated clothing away from flames and guards against ignition by friction or percussion.

(See Manual Sheet SD-42, Sodium Chlorate.)

Chromates

Ammonium, sodium, and potassium chromates, and chromic acid (chromium trioxide) are stable in and of themselves, but are violently reactive as aqueous acid solutions or when brought in contact with organic compounds.

Sodium and potassium dichromates and chromates are widely used in chemical and chemical-consuming industries. In view of their diversified application it is important that personnel handling and using these chemicals be familiar with their chemical behavior and the means by which their potential hazards can be minimized.

Sodium and potassium dichromates and chromates are unregulated by the Interstate Commerce Commission. They are mildly oxidizing in character, but approach the oxidizing power of chromium trioxide in concentrated solutions in the presence of strong acids, e.g., sulfuric acid. The properties of sodium and potassium dichromates and chromates which are important in conjunction with planning for proper handling and use are:

1. They are noncorrosive to metals.
2. They are noncombustible and will not support combustion, but may react slowly with certain organic materials, e.g., they may attack and weaken clothing fibers.
3. They can irritate mucous membranes and skin, and cause ulceration of skin wounds.
4. If inhaled as dust or solution mist, they may irritate the respiratory system.
5. In contact with the eyes, they can cause irritation and conjunctivitis.
6. If ingested, they tend to act as their own emetic and purgative; if retained, stomach and kidney complications can ensue.

Many years of experience have shown that sodium and potassium dichromates and chromates can be handled and used safely by adhering to the precautions detailed in Chemical Safety Data Sheet SD-46, Sodium and Potassium Dichromates and Chromates.

Perchloric Acid

Perchloric acid is generally used as a solution of 60-72% $HClO_4$. Principal laboratory application is in quantitative analytical work.

At elevated temperatures—approximately 160°C (320°F)—it is a dangerously reactive oxidizing agent and a strong dehydrating agent. Vapors of the solution are odorless unless contaminated, and irritate and corrode mucous membranes and skin.

Explosive anhydrous perchloric acid may be formed if perchloric acid solution comes in contact with a dehydrating agent; in fact, most explosions involving solutions of perchloric acid or its derivatives result from the formation of anhydrous perchloric acid or its organic derivatives formed as secondary products. The anhydrous acid is unstable even at room temperatures, eventually decomposing spontaneously with explosive force; in contact with oxidizable material, it explodes at once.

Combustible materials, such as sawdust, excelsior, wood, paper, burlap bags, cotton waste, rags, grease, oil, and most organic compounds, containing perchloric acid solution, are highly flammable and dangerous. They may explode on heating, contact with flame, impact, or from friction; or they may ignite spontaneously. Fires may be controlled with large quantities of water delivered in a solid stream.

In working with perchloric acid solution in the laboratory, these precautions should be taken:

1. Avoid contact with skin or by breathing vapors.

2. Avoid contact with all organic matter unless the materials are known not to react explosively with perchloric acid.

3. Avoid contact of strong dehydrating agents such as concentrated sulfuric acid or phosphorus pentoxide with perchloric acid solutions.

4. Carry out laboratory reactions involving perchloric acid solution in a hood and behind laboratory safety shields.

5. Limit laboratory quantities to one 1-pound reagent bottle per hood. It is good practice to keep the reagent bottle in a hood on a deep glass tray with sufficient capacity to hold the entire contents in case of breakage. The tray and outside of the reagent bottle should be rinsed daily.

To prevent breakage, the larger supply bottle should be carried inside of a spun glass padded container with sufficient capacity to catch the entire contents. It is good practice to pour, over a sink, from the reagent bottle directly into a graduate and thence into the digestion or reaction flask. When the stopper is replaced, the reagent bottle should be rinsed with water and returned to the glass tray. All glass apparatus used should also be rinsed thoroughly after use. The diluted and partially exhausted sample from the digestion or reaction flask should be poured into the drain quantitatively with a large amount of water.

6. The laboratory hoods for perchloric acid vapor should be made of metallic or ceramic materials, supplied with a strong exhaust direct to the roof, and so designed that ducts and hoods can be thoroughly washed with plenty of water. Ducts and hoods should not be permitted to collect dust or residues of any type which might come in contact with the vapor of boiling perchloric acid solution. Residues can be eliminated by daily washing with water. Hoods, in which perchloric acid solution is used, should have separate exhaust systems discharging in a safe location. Perchloric acid vapor should never be allowed to enter air-conditioning systems.

7. Since, in most laboratory applications, perchloric acid solution is heated to temperatures at or near its boiling point, heat-resistant glassware is advisable to minimize breakage from heat strains. Heating should be by electric hot plate—a sand bath heat transmitter is preferable to an oil bath, which should never be used for flasks containing hot concentrated perchloric acid solution.

Glass-to-glass unions—never rubber tubes, stoppers, or stop-cocks—should be employed in assembled apparatus. Grease, including silicone types of lubricants should not be used.

8. Avoid spillage and breakage, since floors or shelves of wood or other combustible material may absorb the perchloric acid solution and later, if heated by a steam radiator, a hot plate, etc., may cause a fire or explosion. Wash up spills immediately, using large quantities of water with repeated mopping up, and final thorough rinsing of the mop or rag used.

(See Manual Sheet SD-11, Perchloric Acid Solution.)

Explosive Power

Many chemicals, in addition to the oxidizing materials previously discussed, are explosive or form compounds that are explosive and should be treated accordingly. A few of the more common examples of this class of hazardous materials follow.

Acetylides

Acetylene, under certain conditions, forms highly explosive metallic compounds such as acetylides of copper, silver, and mercury. Copper acetylides have caused many serious explosions, because they are easily detonated by heat or shock. Copper acetylide is soluble in and is quietly decomposed by hydrochloric acid; hence copper equipment that has been in contact with acetylene, or other equipment in which the presence of acetylides is suspected, should be rinsed with hydrochloric acid before welding or heating to remove traces of acetylide.

Silver Acetylide. Acetylene is sometimes determined analytically by absorption in silver nitrate solution which deposits silver acetylide. Such deposits are explosive when dry; consequently the apparatus used should be kept moist until ready for cleaning. Hydrochloric acid washing is sufficient to clean apparatus containing silver acetylide.

Silver Fulminate and Other Nitrogen-Containing Compounds

Mixtures of silver nitrate, nitric acid, and alcohol are known to form silver fulminate (AgONC) which is highly explosive. Silver oxide in ammonia solution forms AgN_3, black fulminating silver. Mercury or mercury oxide and ammonia or ammonium hydroxide are said to form a highly explosive mercuric oxide on long periods of contact. Iodine in contact with aqueous or alcoholic ammonia forms a black powder, nitrogen iodide monoamine ($N_2H_3I_3$), which, when dried, detonates spontaneously and violently when touched or slightly heated.

Peroxides

Among the peroxides are found some of the most highly explosive materials. Usually most peroxides are safely stored under cool, quiescent conditions, or in dilute solution. Hazards with peroxides can be avoided by use of oxidation inhibitors or by careful temperature control.

Barium Peroxide. Barium peroxide is not explosive like the nonmetallic peroxides, but it can easily be a source of fire if moistened or heated when it comes in contact with combustible material.

Sodium Peroxide. Sodium peroxide is more active than barium peroxide. It is used in Parr bomb methods for the determination of sulfur and chlorine. Explosions occasionally occur with this method because of unforeseen reactions, or because of failure to follow scrupulously the standard procedure. This experiment should always be conducted with the protection of a safety screen and goggles.

Hydrogen Peroxide. Hydrogen peroxide is not explosive in the ordinary 3% pharmaceutical dilution which is further stabilized with acetanilide. Hydrogen peroxide is decomposed by contact with copper or finely divided metals, and its concentrated solutions are explosive, due to decomposition. (See Manual Sheet SD-53, Hydrogen Peroxide.)

Ether Peroxides. Ether peroxides are formed by the oxidation of uninhibited ether. Storing ethyl ether under an inert atmosphere, such as nitrogen, or in contact with copper prevents the formation of peroxides. However, isopropyl ether peroxide has a tendency to form even in the presence of copper. Certain antioxidants, such as monobenzyl-para-aminophenol, prevent its formation. Distillation of ethers tends to concentrate the peroxides in the kettle and, if the distillation is continued to dryness, an explosion may result.

Other Peroxides. Peroxides tend to form from other compounds having an ether group, such as butyl ether, dioxane, and glycol-ethers. It is believed that the hazard of distilling the compounds boiling above 100°C is comparatively small because the high temperature of the distillation decomposes the peroxide as fast as it is formed. However, under vacuum distillation, the temperature may be low enough to make the distillation dangerous. In general, any ether-like compound that gives a strong brown color with aqueous 10% potassium iodide solution should not be distilled without special treatment and precautions.

Peracetic Acid

Peracetic acid is formed by the air-oxidation of acetaldehyde, and under proper conditions it is continuously decomposed to acetic acid. However, if acetic acid containing peracetic acid is distilled, an organic inhibitor such as hydroquinone should be added to prevent the formation of the active peracetic acid.

Organic Nitrogen Compounds

Occasionally such materials as gunpowder, nitroglycerine, dynamite, trinitrotoluene, and picric acid are encountered in the laboratory, but cautious handling and knowledge of their inherent explosive properties can reduce hazardous action to a minimum. These compounds are normally encountered only in specialized laboratories. But if nonspecialists have occasion to deal with them, they should seek proper directions from their supervisor before handling such materials.

Cellulose Nitrate. Cellulose nitrate is highly flammable and contains oxygen to support its own combustion. Carbon dioxide is of little use as a fire extinguisher for this compound; water is an effective extinguishing agent because it helps to cool the material below its fire point. Burning nitrocellulose expels nitrous fumes which are very toxic.

Polymerization

Often encountered in the laboratory are materials which may polymerize on standing. Since most polymerizations are exothermic, spontaneous explosions may result unless the necessary precautions are taken. A few examples would include the polymerization of diketene, ethylene oxide in the presence of powdered potassium hydroxide and vinyl compounds. (See Manual Sheets SD-55, Butadiene and SD-56, Vinyl Chloride.)

Liquid Oxygen

Liquid oxygen and liquid air are likely to produce an explosion when mixed with hydrocarbons or other combustibles. Care should be taken that liquefied petroleum gases are not mixed inadvertently with liquid oxygen or liquid air. When necessary for catalytic reaction purposes, mixing must be done under carefully controlled conditions under proper supervision.

Oxygen and Combustibles

Oil in the presence of oxygen reacts to form oxides at a violent rate with consequent explosion hazard. For this reason no equipment in which oxygen is handled should be lubricated with hydrocarbons or any other material that will burn. Jets of oxygen should never be permitted to strike any oily surface or greasy clothes, or to enter a tank or container that has contained a flammable substance. Valve regulators or other equipment, used for oxygen, should never be used for other gases; nor should equipment used for other gases be transferred to oxygen service.

Chlorine and Ethylene

Chlorine and ethylene have been observed to react violently, exhibiting explosive characteristics when mixed. Under carefully defined and controlled conditions, the gases can be safely mixed, but indiscriminate mixing should be avoided.

Sodium Metal

Potassium and sodium metals and metal hydrides on contact with water produce hydrogen and sufficient heat to ignite the gas with explosive rapidity. Waste scraps of sodium should not be thrown into a trash can or a sink, but should be added in small portions to high boiling alcohols, such as propanol or butanol, and safely disposed of after all action ceases. Larger quantities of sodium should be disposed of under competent supervision in areas away from places of habitation. Only nonaqueous fire extinguishers can be used, such as dry soda ash. (See Manual Sheet SD-47, Sodium, Metallic.)

Calcium Carbide

Calcium carbide reacts with water to form acetylene. Fires from calcium carbide are best fought by smothering them with carbon dioxide or dry sand; water is worse than useless. If no serious hazard exists and the fire can be controlled, it is best to let the fire burn itself out. (See Manual Sheet SD-7, Acetylene.)

CHAPTER VIII

Toxicity

Chemicals frequently used in the laboratory may be inherently hazardous in different degrees. Improper storage and handling can lead to personal injury. Such accidents may be caused by chemicals or their fumes coming in contact with the body, or through inhalation or swallowing.

Hazards of Toxicity

Laboratory chemicals improperly stored or handled can cause injury to personnel by virtue of their toxicity. Such injuries are called toxic or chemical injuries because the living organism is damaged by "chemical" action. This is in contrast to injuries caused by physical forces: mechanical blows, external radiation, and heat.

Different substances possess this property of toxicity in different degrees. Not only are some more potent than others, but, also, different materials produce different types of injury. For example, one may injure the liver or kidneys, whereas another may act upon the brain, with negligible effect on the other organs. The concept of toxicity, therefore, has both a quantitative and qualitative aspect. Differences in both aspects have practical importance.

Quantitative Toxic Effects. The quantitative aspect of toxicity is described in terms of the amount of chemical or the intensity of exposure which produces specified toxic effects or which just fails to produce a toxic effect. The amount of chemical is stated in terms of weight per unit weight of body of the animal or person. Intensity of exposure is given in terms of concentration of toxicant and duration of exposure. Common quantitative measures of toxicity are those doses or intensities of exposure which kill (in experimental studies) 0%, 50%, and 100% of a group of animals. In matters of health and safety are those doses and intensities which just fail to cause injury, commonly referred to as maximum allowable concentrations (MAC).

The ranges from the most toxic to the least toxic are considerable. The maximum dosages which can be swallowed daily without injury will vary from a fraction of a microgram to many grams. Some of the least toxic materials are tolerated at 10% and 20% of the total food intake. Concentrations of contaminant in air which can be tolerated daily range from a small fraction of a microgram per liter (2.2×10^{-9} mg/l for polonium) to a number of milligrams per liter (about 9 mg/l or 5% by volume for carbon dioxide). Some materials—liquid bromine, for example—are so irritating that contact of a few seconds' duration will result in a local burn. Substances at the other end of the range for local irritants will require regular daily contacts each for a full day's duration to produce some local irritation. In the case of substances which are absorbed through the skin, the minimal toxic doses (applied to the skin) will vary from a few milligrams, an amount too small to be noticeable on the skin, to quantities so large as to be unattainable.

Qualitative Toxic Effects. The qualitative aspect of toxicity is described by enumerating the organs or tissues affected and the nature of the toxic changes. The quite varied injuries may be classed as local and as systemic.

Local injuries are those limited to the area of the body that has ome in contact with the toxicant, the most common being the skin and the eyes. Local injury also may be encountered in the nose, throat, and lungs after inhalation of toxicants and in the mouth, throat, stomach, and intestine after swallowing.

Systemic injuries are those produced in any of the organs after the toxicant has been absorbed into the blood stream. Distinctions are made between local and systemic effects because these do not show similar or parallel variations among different chemicals.

Toxic effects, both local and systemic, also show considerable variation as to type, duration, and seriousness to health and life. On the one hand, they may be mild, temporary, and not particularly serious or dangerous to life; whereas, on the other hand, they may be extremely serious in all respects. The nature of the toxic effects determines to a large extent the hazard presented by various toxicants and, accordingly, the precautions to be taken to ensure safety.

Acute and Chronic Toxicity

Chemicals will show a greater or lesser difference in toxicity depending upon whether they act upon the body for a short time or a long time. Thus two substances may have nearly identical degrees of toxicity (equal potency) when inhaled for a single period of time or when swallowed once. Their potency, however, may be greatly different when they are inhaled or swallowed every day for a long period of time. In addition, the nature of the toxic injury produced by a chemical can be quite different depending upon the duration of exposure.

Acute toxicity is defined as that which is manifest on short exposure. "Short exposure" cannot be defined precisely; it is commonly thought of as a single oral intake, a single contact with the skin and eyes, and a single exposure to contaminated air lasting for any period up to about 8 or possibly 24 hours.

Chronic toxicity is defined as that which is manifest when the toxicants act upon the body over a long period of time. The time period and the pattern of exposure cannot be stated precisely; ordinarily they are thought of as regular daily exposures for periods measured in weeks, months, and even years. Some substances—radium, for example—can produce a chronic poisoning after a single dose has been swallowed, because excessive amounts are retained in the body for many years. Other substances must be encountered repeatedly for long periods of time before chronic effects result. Regardless of the exact pattern, chronic toxicity is manifest when the toxicant acts upon the body over a long period of time without significant respite.

Types of Exposure

There are but four types of exposure to chemicals: (1) contact with the skin and the eyes; (2) inhalation; (3) swallowing; and (4) injection. These are listed in order of importance in chemical work.

Contact with Skin and Eyes. Contact with the skin is of first importance because of the frequency with which it occurs; one can say that such contact is the rule in working with chemicals, since truly remarkable precautions are necessary to guarantee no contact at all. The most common result of excessive contact on the skin is a localized irritation or burn. But an appreciable number of materials are absorbed through the skin with sufficient rapidity to produce systemic poisoning.

Contamination of shoes and clothing has particular significance, because the confinement of the toxicant materially increases the severity of exposure and of injury. Some materials, such as the common volatile organic solvents, can be tolerated on the uncovered skin to a considerable extent without injury, but these same materials confined in ordinary clothing can produce irritation and burns. It is not always necessary that the clothing be wet through. Quite potent materials such as dimethyl sulfate can cause burns of disabling extent if but a few drops touch clothing (see Chapter XI on Clothing and Personal Protective Equipment).

Contact of chemicals with the eyes is of particular concern because these organs are so sensitive and because impairment or loss of vision is tragic. Seemingly very few substances are innocuous in contact with the eyes; most are painful and irritating, and a considerable number are capable of causing "burns" and loss of vision.

Inhalation. Inhalation of air contaminated with gas, vapor, dust, or fumes is an exposure which is important in all large-scale operations. Even in small-scale laboratory operations, inhalation of such materials can be an important source of toxicants, since but a few grams or less of many substances can produce excessive contamination.

Swallowing. Swallowing of chemicals must be considered in two categories: (1) willful or accidental, and (2) incidental. The latter is that which occurs from exposure to air contaminated with dust and fumes, from contamination of hands and face, and from contamination of food and drink in the work area. These occur incidentally in working with chemicals. Such incidental ingestion is important with the more toxic materials—lead, arsenic, etc.—which occur as dusts and fumes.

Willful swallowing is of course not a matter for those concerned with laboratory safety; therefore, oral ingestion will not be considered in this chapter. Accidental swallowing is not a common laboratory hazard, and such accidents can be prevented by prohibiting use of laboratory beakers and the like for drinking water, coffee, and other beverages.

Injection. Injection of chemicals would appear to be a type of exposure which could not occur in the chemical laboratory. The equivalent, however, can happen rather readily through mechanical injuries with glass or metal contaminated with chemicals. Contamination of open wounds may be the equivalent. Outright injection may result in work at high pressures—a small leak will produce a "stream" of liquid material of sufficient force to penetrate the skin.

Warning Senses

Two sensory effects—smell and pain—have a certain usefulness to the chemist in that they warn of the exposure to many toxicants.

The sense of smell can be very helpful in preventing excessive exposure to the gas or vapor of some materials. Limitations of this warning effect must be understood, however. Some substances are not detected by smell or only at concentrations considerably above safe levels; some substances, on the other hand, are detectable at such low levels that the warning has no practical value; and finally, the sense of smell often is lost through fatigue or paralysis, or it is too weak to be a satisfactory warning.

The sense of pain tends to be more dependable than the sense of smell. Useful sensations of pain occur in the skin, eyes, and breathing passages (nose, throat, and chest). These sensations may be caused by gases, vapors, solids, or liquids dispersed in air. Pain warns of exposure and, when it occurs promptly at appropriate concentrations and with adequate severity, it is effective in preventing excessive exposure. With a substance such as hydrochloric acid, no one will voluntarily tolerate exposure to dangerous concentrations. With many substances, however, pain will be capable of warning of the presence of a toxicant, but it will not be severe enough to "drive one out."

In a certain sense toxic effects can serve as warning signals. When the initial toxic injury occurs promptly and is not of serious nature, it can serve quite effectively to warn of exposure before a serious poisoning is produced. There are many toxic chemicals that send out such alarms. With a number of materials, however, no warning whatever will be experienced during exposure, and serious and even fatal injury can result.

These warning properties are quite useful in favorable circumstances and with a limited number of toxicants whose properties are well understood. The senses, however, cannot be relied upon for protection in working with new substances.

Tolerance and Sensitivity

Among "normal" healthy human subjects (and animals) there is a considerable difference in susceptibility; not all subjects experience the same degree of injury from the same amount of toxicant or same intensity of exposure. A dose or exposure affecting the most resistant individual may be 10 times as great as that affecting the most susceptible.

Aside from this natural variation among apparently healthy subjects of the same species, certain conditions and diseases may increase the susceptibility of individuals. Actually but little specific information is available on this subject, so that its importance cannot be stated exactly. It seems reasonable that any one illness or disability which tends to weaken the body would lessen the resistance toward toxicants. Experience, however, has not indicated a serious or widespread problem.

One particular relationship should be noted: Persons who have or have had asthma may suffer asthmatic attacks following exposures to "irritants," whereas "normal" subjects are not affected by these same exposures.

The combined toxic action of two or more chemicals also is the subject of speculation and some concern. It is well known in the field of medicine that certain pairs of drugs will act together; the separate actions combine or one reinforces the other. In some instances the combined action may be much greater than that to be obtained by the simple addition of the separate actions; this is "potentiation" or "synergism." Again, there is but a limited amount of specific information on this phenomenon. Whereas experience does not indicate a widespread or serious problem from exposure to two or more chemicals, there are a few cases of apparent potentiation. It seems rather certain that ingestion of alcohol increases susceptibility to carbon tetrachloride.

Among large numbers of apparently normal subjects there are customarily a few who show an unusually high susceptibility regardless of the chemicals involved. These people are said to be naturally hypersensitive. They respond adversely to substances, or to exposures, which are quite harmless to the majority of persons.

A number of chemicals have the property of inducing this hypersensitivity. Individuals exposed for a time to these substances, even without apparent injury, subsequently become hypersensitive and are affected adversely by exposures which previously were not harmful. The hypersensitivity may be so extreme that even minute amounts of the chemical are harmful.

The skin is the organ which most commonly develops a hypersensitivity to chemicals. In some instances, other organs or tissues may respond as well as the skin; there may be systemic illness. Less frequently this hypersensitivity develops in the breathing passages or lungs, with the result that an asthma-like response is produced.

Continued exposure to some chemicals, however, results in an increased resistance or tolerance, in contrast to hypersensitivity.

Difference Between Hazard and Toxicity

The frequency, duration, and concentration of an exposure determines the potential hazard of personnel working with given toxic chemicals. It is self-evident that the chemical inside a closed container resting on the shelf or in the storeroom will never injure anyone. Injury cannot occur without exposure.

In the actual manufacture, handling, and use of chemicals, the nature of the operations determines the amount of exposure. The presence of 5 ml of a liquid in a small test tube will obviously result in less contamination of the air than will the exposure of 10 or 100 gallons in open buckets or tanks. The handling and use of 5 gm of solid material in the test tube causes much less contact upon the skin than does the transfer of 5 lb from a carton to reactor or the grinding of 5 lb in a mill.

Furthermore, physical properties influence or determine the amounts of exposure. In any one situation, the material with a boiling point of 35°C at 760 mm Hg will cause much more contamination of air and resultant inhalation of vapor than will the material with a boiling point of 241°C. Liquid substances, upon immediate intimate contact with the skin, can spread much more than do large pieces of solid matter. In other instances, the dusty solid escaping into the air of the work space will produce more skin contact than does the high-boiling liquid which cannot escape into the air so as to contact the skin.

In any case of exposure, however, injury (poisoning) will not occur unless that exposure is excessive. If the use of a dusty solid results in the daily inhalation and swallowing of 0.2 mg of a chemical, poisoning will result only if 0.2 mg daily is toxic. Poisoning will not result if the smallest toxic dose is greater than this amount. Similarly the inhalation of 80 ppm of vapor 8 hours daily, or contact of a 0.5% solution upon the skin for 15 minutes, will cause injury only if these exposures exceed safe limits.

Thus we see that not only the toxicity of chemicals, but also chemical and physical properties, and the nature and circumstances of handling and use determine whether or not chemicals will cause injury. Unfortunately, in many cases it cannot be determined with absolute certainty that poisoning will or will not occur. As indicated previously, the susceptibility of different subjects varies; furthermore, different people performing the same work will experience different intensities of exposures, and circumstances vary with time. Accordingly, it is the likelihood or probability of poisoning with which we must deal. This likelihood is termed "hazard."

It is most important that the concept of hazard and its distinction from toxicity be clearly understood. Among chemicals in general, hazard does not always vary in direct proportion with toxicity. Further, for any one substance, hazard will vary considerably in different circumstances. And, finally, it is the ability to control the hazard through proper handling procedures, sound engineering design, and the use of protective equipment that permits the safe use of chemicals regardless of degree of toxicity.

Use of Toxicological Information

Toxicological information on chemicals is available to a considerable and an increasing extent. This information, recorded in a number of books and journals such as those listed in "Literature References," comes from two fields: from experience in manufacture and use of chemicals, and from animal experiments. The extent of the information varies considerably, but all of it, when applied intelligently, aids greatly in achieving safe operation.

To the greatest extent, human experience, as recorded, describes the qualitative aspect of toxicity. Data on intensities of exposure are inadequate. In the case of a number of the older and more common industrial chemicals—e.g., chlorine and lead compounds—there seems to be a reasonably accurate indication of the degree of chronic toxicity. This finds expression in the form of industrial hygiene standards. With but very few substances has human experience yielded a satisfactory estimate of both acute and chronic toxicity.

Experiments upon laboratory animals must be relied upon entirely for information on the toxicity of new chemicals. The application of such experiments to industrial chemical problems has increased greatly during the last twenty years. The experience gained in this time has demonstrated the practical value of the data from animal experiments; an experienced industrial toxicologist can supply information from animal experiments which can assure high safety in work with chemicals.

The application of toxicological information to specific questions must be made with considerable personal judgment. As indicated in the discussion of hazard, allowance must be made for the various factors which influence the nature and intensity of exposure. The application to human subjects of data from animal experiments must be made tentatively until verification has been obtained through experience. In this application some allowance must be made for possible differences in susceptibility, but there is no justification for the arbitrary application of very large "factors of safety."

For a number of older materials which have been encountered frequently as contaminants of the workroom air, both as gases and particulate matter, there are lists of Industrial Hygiene Standards, commonly referred to in the past as "Maximum Allowable Concentrations." These standards represent the highest concentrations of contaminant acceptable for regular daily exposures of up to 8-hours' duration each.

Such Industrial Hygiene Standards are listed by a number of different individuals and groups, both official and nonofficial. One must recognize that, although these standards are based upon toxicological data and experience, at the same time they are to a large extent matters of personal opinion, and subject to change. Further, they may be based upon comfort (pleasantness) as much as upon toxicity. In some instances, but not in others, the numerical values may be determined by the application of a "safety factor." In no case have these safety factors been adequately described or defined, nor have supporting data been given. These standards, however, must be considered to represent informed opinion and, in the hands of the experienced industrial hygienist, they are useful tools in preventing excessive exposures. (See pages 141-144.)

Illustrative Materials

In the following section are descriptions of the toxic properties and recommended precautions for a number of typical chemicals as these apply to handling and to industrial and laboratory type operations. The precautions do not apply to exposures that result from so called "consumer" products.

The information on skin and eye irritation relates to the undiluted chemical except when specifically stated otherwise. This convention must be followed, because the irritating actions of different substances do not decrease uniformly upon dilution.

The precautions to a large extent must be stated in terms of end to be accomplished. The exact measure to be taken will depend upon circumstances; for example, adequate protection of the eyes may be obtained in one case by the use of safety goggles, whereas in other circumstances a full face gas mask or helmet may be required.

Sodium Hydroxide (Caustic Soda, Lye)

Sodium hydroxide is a strong local irritant to all tissues. This action is exhibited by all forms of the solid and by solutions of high dilution. Concentrated material produces burns very rapidly. Sodium hydroxide presents no problem of systemic poisoning. (See Chapter VII on Chemical Hazards.)

Contact in the Eyes. All forms, even solutions as dilute as 1%, are capable of producing serious injury upon short contacts. The danger is particularly great because of the rapid penetration of the tissues of the eye. Hot caustic will produce almost instant destruction of the tissues.

Contact with the Skin. Sodium hydroxide is irritating to the skin as much as to the eyes, but the action is somewhat slower. Occasional short contacts, even with concentrated material, can be tolerated without injury. Prolonged contact leads to irritation and burns depending upon concentration. Any solution of pH greater than about 10 can be irritating. Dust of the solid material causes a burning sensation and small red inflamed spots.

Exposure to Dust in the Air. The fine dust is painful to the nose and to the skin. There is no problem of systemic poisoning, nor apparently of injury to the lungs, since excessive exposure cannot be tolerated.

Precautions. Because of the seriousness of the local injury to skin and eyes, and the rapidity with which it causes damage, extensive precautions are recommended to prevent contact and ample provision should be made to permit immediate removal of caustic from skin and eyes, in the event of accidental exposure.

The exact measures will be determined primarily by the nature of operations. Always, the eyes should have protection adequate for the severity of exposures that can occur. Safety goggles, face or eye shields, and chemical workers' goggles are commonly used. Appropriate protective gloves and other garments of rubber should be worn to prevent contact on skin and clothing.

Irritating quantities of dust and mist should be kept out of the work atmosphere.

Phenol (Carbolic Acid)

Phenol is considered a quite hazardous material through contact with the skin and eyes. It produces local injury (burns) and is rapidly absorbed through the skin in toxic amounts. There is no serious problem of inhalation at ordinary temperatures and in open work areas. (See Chemical Safety Data Sheet SD-4.)

Contact in the Eyes. Phenol rapidly produces more or less serious injury to the eyes depending upon concentration of material and duration of contact. Concentrated material promptly causes burns with possible impairment of vision. Prompt, thorough washing with water will mitigate greatly the consequences of contact.

Contact with the Skin. Phenol also is strongly irritating to the skin. Concentrated material will produce a burn (denaturation) of the skin within a few minutes. Solutions as dilute as 1% also will cause irritation and burns when confined to the skin for prolonged periods (hours). Such contact could result from contamination of shoes and clothing.

Phenol also presents a serious hazard of acute systemic poisoning by absorption through the skin. This hazard is very real when working with more than a few milliliters of concentrated material. The contamination of an area no greater than that of the hand or forearm will permit the absorption of toxic and fatal amounts within a matter of minutes (possibly no more than 10 to 15). Toxic amounts likewise are absorbed from concentrations as low as 1% provided contact is sufficiently extensive and prolonged.

Prompt removal of phenol by washing with large amounts of water, or soap and water, can prevent all injury except possibly a minor local irritation (see Chapter XI on Clothing and Personal Protective Equipment).

Exposure to Contaminated Air. Significant contamination of the air of the open work space will occur only when phenol is heated or, possibly, if large amounts of phenol are exposed in small unventilated spaces.

An Industrial Hygiene Standard of 5 ppm has been suggested as a safe limit for regular daily exposures.

Precautions. Because of the seriousness of the local injury to skin and eyes, and the danger of systemic poisoning, extensive precautions should be taken to prevent local contact upon the person. In addition, there should be provision for washing facilities for the eyes and skin to permit immediate removal of phenol in the event of accidental exposure.

Painful amounts of vapor should be kept out of the workroom air. The hood should be used for small-scale operations with heated phenol. In large-scale operations, special enclosures and exhaust ventilation may be required.

Nitric Acid (Fuming, and 5% or Higher)

Fuming nitric acid rapidly attacks all tissues, literally destroying them, unless removed very quickly. In addition, exposure of the acid to the air, as well as chemical reactions, releases a mixture of highly toxic nitrogen oxides.

Contact in the Eyes. This concentrated acid attacks the eyes quite rapidly and will produce severe burns with impairment or loss of vision. Immediate washing of the contaminated eyes with water will mitigate damage.

Contact with the Skin. Similarly, this acid attacks the skin with great rapidity. Within seconds there results a smarting sensation and yellow coloration. If the acid is not removed promptly, severe, deep, and painful burns result. Immediate removal may leave a yellow coloration of the skin with subsequent peeling.

Exposure to Contaminated Air. The mixture of nitrogen oxides escaping from fuming nitric acid readily produces a serious and even fatal localized injury in the lungs. A few liters of acid spilled upon the floor can produce sufficient contamination in the area to cause serious injury on short, single exposures. These oxides also are evolved in considerable volume when nitric acid reacts with certain metals and with any organic matter (see Nitric Acid in Chapter VII).

Some injury may result from single prolonged exposure (8 hours) to concentrations as low as 25 ppm of some of the oxides. Some hundreds of parts per million (200-700 ppm) may cause injury on but a few inhalations. These oxides are particularly hazardous because there is no effective warning of exposure and because illness becomes apparent suddenly after a delay of as long as 48 hours.

Because of this delayed appearance of injury, persons known or suspected to have been exposed appreciably to nitrogen oxides should be placed in the care of an informed physician even though they feel quite well. Prompt treatment before illness develops may completely avert otherwise serious or fatal injury to the lungs.

Precautions. Because of the promptness with which injury is produced and the seriousness of the injury, extensive precautions should be taken to prevent contact in the eyes and on the skin. In addition there should be facilities for washing both eyes and skin to permit immediate removal of the acid in the event of accidental contact.

Precautions should be taken to keep the oxides of nitrogen out of the workroom air. Except for micro-scale operations, fuming nitric acid should be used in the hood. With operations too large for the hood, control may be obtained by enclosure and exhaust ventilation. Special provision should be made to dilute and wash away spilled acid without exposure to the fumes. (See Chemical Safety Data Sheet SD-5 and Chapter VII of this volume.)

Bromine

Liquid bromine presents serious hazards of local injury at the area of contact and of injury to the lungs from inhalation of vapor.

Contact in the Eyes. Liquid bromine is so reactive that it produces burns immediately upon contact. Prompt, thorough flushing of the eyes with water followed by proper medical treatment will lessen but not prevent injury.

Contact with the Skin. Liquid bromine attacks the skin at once; it quickly produces deep burns that heal slowly. Prompt removal of the bromine by washing with water will lessen the extent of injury.

Exposure to Contaminated Air. Bromine vapor is very similar to chlorine gas in its toxic properties. The painful effect upon the eyes may be apparent at concentrations as low as about 0.3 ppm under some conditions. Bromine vapors seem to be less painful to the upper breathing passages of the head and neck, at least pain and coughing develop much more slowly. Excessive inhalation leads to the same sort of injury to the lungs, nose, and throat as that produced by chlorine.

For regular daily exposures, bromine vapor must be kept at levels which are not painful; generally this will be less than 1 ppm.

Precautions. Persons handling bromine always should wear proper protective devices for the eyes. Micro-operations may be carried out with bare hands, but rubber gloves and laboratory aprons should be worn for larger scale operations. Persons handling bottles and larger quantities should be protected by goggles and/or face shields, heavy rubber gloves, aprons, and boots. Facilities for washing the eyes and the skin should be immediately available.

Laboratory operations on other than a micro-scale should be carried out in a hood to control vapors. Operations too large for a hood require special measures to confine vapors and exhaust ventilation if bromine must be exposed to the air. (See Chemical Safety Data Sheet SD-49.)

Calcium Chloride (Anhydrous)

Anhydrous calcium chloride is a strongly hygroscopic salt which is capable of causing local irritation to the skin and eyes.

Contact in the Eyes. The dry salt causes considerable pain and some inflammation but is not apt to cause serious injury.

Contact with the Skin. The dry salt is somewhat irritating to the skin. In large-scale operations where dust escapes into the air, some persons may experience a local rash at ankles, wrists, or neck. No difficulty is experienced if operations are reasonably clean.

Exposure to Contaminated Air. Fine dust is painful to the nose; it may produce a local inflammation but will not cause serious or systemic injury.

Precautions. No precautions are necessary at bench work in the laboratory. In large-scale operations there may be a need to control dust and to minimize skin contact. Protection of the eyes is advisable.

Aniline

Aniline has no appreciable local irritating action. It does have a dangerous systemic toxicity which may result from inhalation of vapors or from absorption through the skin following contact with liquid material.

Contact in the Eyes. Aniline has no significant irritating action upon the eyes. This does not mean, however, that contamination of the eyes should not be avoided.

Contact with the Skin. Aniline has no significant irritating action upon the skin, but it is readily absorbed through the skin in toxic amounts.

A few drops of aniline remaining on the skin are sufficient to produce marked cyanosis—a bluish coloration of skin, lips, and whites of the eyes. Contact with but a few milliliters is sufficient to produce serious poisoning. This cyanosis is due to the conversion of the blood hemoglobin to a darker colored derivative which does not function as a carrier of oxygen. As a rule injury by aniline is due to this action. In cases of exposure to quite large amounts of aniline, the circulation of blood may fail as a result of other toxic actions.

Exposure to Contaminated Air. Inhalation of aniline vapor produces the same systemic toxic effects as does absorption through the skin. For regular daily operations, vapor concentrations in the work space should be kept at less than 5 ppm.

Precautions. Precautions must be taken to prevent contacts with even as little as a few drops of undiluted aniline. Facilities for washing the eyes and skin should be immediately available in the event of accidental contact.

Aniline should be handled and used so as to keep vapors out of the workroom air. Small-scale operations may be carried out in the hood; large-scale operations require work in closed systems and local exhaust to control vapors. There is considerable advantage in having workmen trained to watch each other for cyanosis, since this condition can develop without the awareness of the individual. (See Chemical Safety Data Sheet SD-17.)

THRESHOLD LIMIT VALUES FOR 1953

Adopted at the Meeting of the American Conference of Governmental Industrial Hygienists, Los Angeles, April, 1953

Values are given in the following tabulation for the maximum average atmospheric concentration of contaminants to which workers may be exposed for an 8-hour working day without injury to health.

These values are based on the best available information from industrial experience, from experimental studies, and, when possible, from a combination of the two. They are not fixed values but are reviewed annually by the Committee on Threshold Limits for changes, revisions, or additions as further information becomes available. Threshold limits should be used as guides in the control of health hazards and should not be regarded as fine lines between safe and dangerous concentrations. They represent conditions only within which it is felt that workers may be repeatedly exposed, day after day, without their health being adversely affected. It is felt, at the present time, that workers should not be exposed to a working environment containing any of these substances in excess of the value indicated.

GASES AND VAPORS

SUBSTANCE	PPM	SUBSTANCE	PPM
Acetaldehyde	200	Cresol	5
Acetic acid	10	Cyclohexane	400
Acetic anhydride	5	Cyclohexanol	100
†Acetone	1,000	Cyclohexanone	100
Acrolein	0.5	Cyclohexene	400
Acrylonitrile	20	Cyclopropane (propene)	400
Ammonia	100	*1-2 Dibromoethane	
Amyl acetate	200	(ethylene dibromide)	25
Isoamyl alcohol	100	o-Dichlorobenzene	50
Aniline	5	Dichlorodifluoro-	
Arsine	0.05	methane	1,000
Benzine (benzol)	35	1,1-Dichloroethane	100
Bromine	1	†1,2-Dichloroethane	
1,3-Butadiene	1,000	(ethylene dichloride)	100
n-Butanol	100	1,2-Dichloroethylene	200
2-Butanone	250	Dichloroethyl ether	15
n-Butyl acetate	200	Dichloromethane	500
Butyl Cellosolve		Dichloromonofluoro-	
(2-butoxyethanol)	200	methane	1,000
Carbon dioxide	5,000	1,1-Dichloro-1-nitro-	
Carbon disulfide	20	ethane	10
Carbon monoxide	100	1,2-Dichloropropane	
†Carbon tetrachloride	25	(propylene dichlo-	
Cellosolve (2-ethoxy-		ride)	75
ethanol)	200	Dichlorotetrafluoro-	
Cellosolve acetate	100	ethane	1,000
Chlorine	1	Diethylamine	25
Chlorobenzene	75	Dimethylaniline	5
2-Chlorobutadiene	25	Dimethylsulfate	1
Chloroform	100	Dioxane	100
1-Chloro-1-nitropro-		Ethyl acetate	400
pane	20	Ethyl alcohol	1,000

* New values.
† Changes from the 1952 list.

SUBSTANCE	PPM	SUBSTANCE	PPM
Ethylamine	25	Methyl iso-butyl ketone	100
Ethyl benzene	200	Naphtha (coal tar)	200
Ethyl bromide	200	Naphtha (petroleum)	500
Ethyl chloride	1,000	Nickel carbonyl	1
Ethylene chlorohydrin	5	Nitrobenzene	1
Ethylene oxide	100	Nitroethane	100
Ethyl ether	400	Nitrogen oxides (other	
Ethyl formate	100	than N_2O)	25
Ethyl silicate	100	Nitroglycerin	0.5
*Fluorine	0.1	Nitromethane	100
Fluorotrichloromethane	1,000	2-Nitropropane	50
Formaldehyde	5	Nitrotoluene	5
Gasoline	500	Octane	500
Heptane	500	Ozone	1
Hexane	500	Pentane	1,000
Hydrogen chloride	5	Pentanone (methyl	
Hydrogen cyanide	10	propanone)	200
Hydrogen fluoride	3	Phenol	5
Hydrogen selenide	0.05	Phosgene	1
Hydrogen sulfide	20	Phosphine	0.05
Iodine	1	Phosphorus trichloride	0.5
Isophorone	25	Propyl acetate	200
Isopropyl alcohol	400	Stibine	0.1
Isopropyl ether	500	Stoddard solvent	500
Mesityl oxide	50	Styrene monomer	200
Methanol	200	Sulfur chloride	1
Methyl acetate	200	Sulfur dioxide	10
Methylal	1,000	1,1,2,2-Tetrachloro-	
Methyl bromide	20	ethane	5
Methyl butanone	100	†Tetrachloroethylene	200
Methyl Cellosolve		Toluene	200
(2-methoxyethanol)	25	Toluidine	5
Methyl Cellosolve		*1-1-1 Trichloroethane	
acetate	25	(methyl chloroform)	500
Methyl chloride	100	†Trichloroethylene	200
Methylcyclohexane	500	Turpentine	100
Methylcyclohexanol	100	Vinyl chloride	500
Methylcyclohexanone	100	Xylene	200
Methyl formate	100		

TOXIC DUSTS, FUMES, AND MISTS

SUBSTANCE	MG PER CU M	SUBSTANCE	MG PER CU M
Antimony	0.5	Pentachloro naphthalene	0.5
Arsenic	0.5	Pentachlorophenol	0.5
Barium	0.5	Phosphorus (yellow)	0.1
Cadmium	0.1	Phosphorus pentachlo-	
Chlorodiphenyl	1	ride	1
Chromic acid and chro-		Phosphorus penta-	
mates as CrO_3	0.1	sulfide	1
Cyanide as CN	5	Selenium, as Se	0.1
*O,O-Diethyl-O-p-nitro-		Sulfuric acid	1
phenyl thiophosphate		Tellurium	0.1
(parathion)	0.1	Tetryl	1.5
Dinitrotoluene	1.5	Trichloronaphthalene	5
o-Dinitrocresol	0.2	Trinitrotoluene	1.5
Fluoride	2.5	*Uranium (soluble	
Iron oxide fume	15	compounds)	0.05
Lead	0.15	*Uranium (insoluble	
Magnesium oxide fume	15	compounds)	0.25
Manganese	6	Zinc oxide fume	15
Mercury	0.1		

MINERAL DUSTS

SUBSTANCE	MPPCF‡	SUBSTANCE	MPPCF
Alundum	50	Silica	
Asbestos	5	high (above 50% free SiO_2)	5
Carborundum	50		
Dust (nuisance, no free silica)	50	medium (5 to 50% free SiO_2)	20
Mica (below 5% free silica)	20	low (below 5% free SiO_2)	50
Portland cement	50	Slate (below 5% free SiO_2)	50
Talc	20	Soapstone (below 5% free SiO_2)	20
		Total dust (below 5% free SiO_2)	50

Radiations

MATERIAL OR RADIATION		MATERIAL OR RADIATION	
Gamma (roentgens per week)	0.3	Roentgen (roentgens per week)	0.3

‡ MPPCF—million particles per cubic foot

CHAPTER IX

Radiation Safety and Contamination Control in the Laboratory

Introduction

Man's experience with radioactivity and penetrating **radiation** in excess of that normally present at the earth's surface dates from the discovery of X-rays by Roentgen in 1895 and the discovery of natural radioactivity by Becquerel in 1896. Except for a comparatively few laboratory workers and X-ray technicians, however, the problems and hazards associated with such radiations did not concern many individuals until the advent of the Atomic Energy Commission program, when comparatively large numbers of workers, technicians, and scientists became involved in projects where such radiation was a continuous part of the production problem. In addition to these AEC workers, the number of individuals in the chemical laboratories and elsewhere who will need to be concerned with the problems involved will necessarily increase as a result of the present proposed widespread use of the radioisotopes produced either as by-products of the over-all Atomic Energy program or as primary production goals.

Tissue and Cell Damage

Soon after the recognition of these radiations, it was found that they could destroy or damage body cells. As in most other cases of cell damage, the body can usually readily repair or replace such injured cells unless the rate of damage exceeds the bodily reparative function or the initial damage is so great that repair is impossible. However, in some parts of the body it was found that such repairs were not apparently being completed and that small amounts of damage produced over a long period of time were cumulative in effect.

Radiation "Tolerance"

As in most matters concerning people, it was soon discovered that the human body's sensitivity to damage from these penetrating radiations varied from person to person. However, it has been possible to establish, with a fair degree of accuracy, an upper limit to the rate at which the body may be continuously irradiated over a period of many years without producing effects which may be clinically detected, much less present the possibility of producing injury. If this limit is reduced by a factor of approximately 10, the value thus obtained is called the maximum permissible dose; and, in all operations where radiation is a problem, efforts are made to maintain working conditions such that the continuous total body irradiation of the persons involved will be less than this figure. Thus, even though short-term exposures of individuals to radiation in excess of the maximum permissible dose may occasionally be necessary, their subsequent possible exposure is usually reduced so that, over a longer period of time, the average value is not greater than that specified as the tolerance.

Maximum Permissible Dose

At present, it is widely considered that a radiation exposure of 300 milliroentgens[1] per week to the entire body or 1500 milliroentgens per week to the hands and forearms are acceptable permissible doses. It should be noted that the earth's surface is continuously bathed with low levels of penetrating radiation of the order of 5 to 20 milliroentgens per week, this radiation re-

---

[1] A milliroentgen is 0.001 roentgen. The roentgen is defined as the amount of radiation which, by ionization, will produce 1 esu of charge per cm³ of air. On the average, 1 roentgen will release approximately 93 ergs of energy per gram of tissue. Since the term roentgen refers only to gamma or X-rays, two other terms frequently used include the "rep" (roentgen equivalent physical) and the "rem" (roentgen equivalent man) which are concerned, respectively, with the equivalent ionization produced by and the relative biological effectiveness of types of radiation other than gamma rays or X-rays. For convenience, the term roentgen, or milliroentgen, will be used in this chapter.

sulting both from cosmic rays and from the presence in the earth's crust of small quantities of radioactive materials.

Definition of Radiation Rays

The radiations emitted by naturally radioactive material are called alpha, beta, and gamma rays. Alpha rays are streams of heavy, positively charged particles which have been identified as helium nuclei. Similarly, beta rays are composed of streams of lighter, negatively charged particles which have been identified as electrons. Gamma rays and X-rays were identified as true electromagnetic waves such as light, but with the distinguishing characteristics of higher frequency and much greater penetrating ability.

Although certain other types of particle radiation have been found to be emitted by the artificially-produced radioisotopes now available, it should be noted that they do not occur very frequently and that present methods for controlling beta and alpha radiations are also effective for them.[2]

Detection by Human Senses

From the viewpoint of providing protection to laboratory workers, it should be pointed out that the presence of none of these radiations may be detected by any of the human senses, and that their ability to penetrate matter is one of their most distinguishing characteristics.

Effective Distance of Travel of Alpha, Beta, Gamma, or X-ray Particles

Alpha particles can travel only about 1 inch in air and have very little penetrating effect, a piece of paper or the dead outer layer of the human skin being sufficient to stop even the most energetic of them. Beta particles, on the other hand, may have a

---

[2] Problems associated with neutrons are not considered further, since, in general, neutron emission occurs only during nuclear reactions or under other specially designed conditions. However, it may be noted that neutrons will affect photographic film, that they will damage tissue, and that shielding therefrom depends upon the nuclear properties of the substances used. Water, paraffin, cadmium, and boron are examples of materials that are considered effective.

range up to 30 feet in air. The most energetic can penetrate the skin and tissue about ⅓ of an inch. However, they may be almost completely stopped by ⅛ inch of aluminum, ½ inch of Lucite, or similar materials. Gamma rays or X-rays cannot be entirely stopped, but they will be attenuated, or their intensity will be reduced, as they pass through matter, the amount of this attenuation depending primarily upon the area density (measured in g/cm² or lb/ft²) of the material concerned and the energy of the radia-

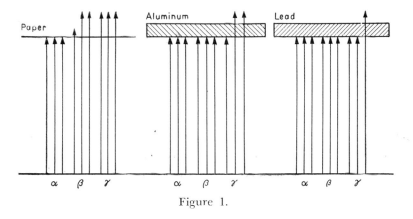

Figure 1.

tions. Figure 1 indicates schematically these penetration effects for alpha, beta, and gamma radiations.

Biological Effects

Although all of these radiations produce injury by cellular damage as a result of their ionizing properties, such radiobiological damage is also somewhat dependent upon the type of radiation concerned. Thus, it is now considered that ionizations produced by gamma rays and beta particles have relatively the same biological effect, but that the ionization produced by alpha particles is relatively about 10 times as effective as is that produced by beta and gamma radiation.

Body Absorption of Radiation

If materials emitting any of these radiations are taken into the body, their absorption and deposition in the body organs will depend upon their chemical properties as with nonradioactive materials. The organs in which they are deposited will thus be constantly irradiated and the cells may be damaged. The radioactive decay of the substance will aid the natural eliminative processes in removing the radiation from the organ concerned, but for the longer-lived radioisotopes, this decay is of very little importance.

Since the alpha particles themselves cannot penetrate the outer skin, it should be noted that alpha-emitting materials are not hazardous if kept outside the body; beta and gamma radiations, on the other hand, are hazardous whether the emitting material is inside or outside of the body.

CONTROL MEASURES

General

Although a great variety of radioactive isotopes are now available, it should be emphasized that their radiations are all essentially of the types discussed above and that the differences in shielding and other methods of handling in actual practice will be based primarily on the type of radiation, the energies of the particles or radiations involved, and the total activities of the material concerned; the general methods of control for each type of radiation will not need to be altered. The chemical and toxic hazards associated with these radioactive isotopes will be the same as they are for the normal stable isotopes of the material concerned.

Various publications and charts, some of which are listed in the appendix, give the types of radiation and the energies that may be anticipated from any given radioactive isotopes, and methods of computing shielding are available. It should be noted that when shielding or other control measures are planned, protection considerations should be based on the complete range of radiations resulting from the radioactive decay series of the original material concerned. As an example, ruthenium-106 has only a very low energy beta emission, but its daughter, rhodium-106, emits both high energy beta and gamma rays. Specific information on the properties and hazards of these various isotopes is, in general, available from the supplier. The National Bureau of Standards Handbooks No. 42 and No. 52 also provide such information.

Penetrating Radiation

Where possible, distance between the source and the worker is probably the best and cheapest method of preventing personnel exposure to excessive penetrating radiation. If maintenance of the large distances that may be necessary is not feasible, shielding is required.

As has been indicated, beta particles may be almost completely stopped by a properly chosen thickness of such materials as aluminum, glass, various plastics, etc. However, a factor that may prove complicating in beta-shielding is the fact that in stopping high energy particles, some materials give off secondary low energy gamma rays, which, in their turn, may require additional shielding before being reduced to safe levels.

For gamma rays, dense materials, such as lead, are usually necessary for adequate shielding if it is desirable that the shield be thin, or concrete may be used if shield thickness is not of primary concern or if rigidity is a factor.

Holes in a shield may give rise to localized beams of radiation escaping into the working area. Thus, if it becomes necessary to penetrate a shield for any reason, such as the insertion of control rods, care should be taken to see that the shield "hole" thus produced does not permit excessive radiation in the operating regions.

It should also be pointed out that penetrating radiations are scattered by many substances. Thus, even though an adequate shield between an operator and the source is provided, the working area should be carefully monitored during a typical operation or when changes in adjacent areas are made to see that the radiation level in the working location is not above the specified limits.

It is difficult to provide personnel equipment that is adequate for protection against penetrating radiation. However, lead-lined or lead-impregnated materials have been used with some success for protection against beta particles and low energy gamma rays, even though the weight and necessary clumsiness involved are distinct disadvantages and usually limit the protection to a part of the body only. An example of the type of protection thus afforded is that provided by lead-impregnated X-ray technicians' gloves.

Since radiation exposure depends not only upon the rate at which a body is being irradiated (or the intensity of the field where work is done), but also upon the length of time during which such irradiation occurs, it is perhaps obvious that another way of controlling personnel exposure to radiation is the limitation of time during which an individual works in a given radiation field. Thus, an employee working in a radiation field of 10 mr/hr for 3 hours receives the same radiation exposure as one working for 1 hour in a 30 mr/hr field.

CONTAMINATION

Definition

Contamination, for purposes of this discussion, is defined as the presence of unwanted and unconfined radioactive materials. In radiochemical laboratories, contamination may be encountered on tools, glassware, working surfaces, clothing, hands, biological materials, waste, and in the air. It becomes evident that contamination may easily be unwittingly transferred from one object to another. Thus, unless adequate precautions to control contamination are taken, some radioactive material may find its way into the body by inhalation, ingestion, or through cuts and abrasions on exposed areas of the skin. For some materials, absorption through intact skin is also possible.

Elimination of Internal Radiation

Since the only methods by which this internal radiation may be removed from the body involve natural body elimination, which is frequently uncertain, and radioactive decay, which for the long-lived radioisotopes is extremely slow, reliance should not be placed upon these processes as protective measures.

Safeguards Against Body Intake

Operating procedures designed to prevent the spread of radioactive contamination are of prime importance in health hazard considerations. Especially is this true for alpha-emitting materials which, although not hazardous if kept outside the body, present special problems if deposited in a body organ because of the high radiobiological effectiveness of the alpha particles.

Safeguards Against Radioactive Dusts

Experiments have shown that, in general, materials inhaled as dusts or taken in through wounds are more readily dissolved into the blood stream and deposited in the body than are materials ingested. Thus, the maintenance of a clean working location with especial attention paid to keeping the air uncontaminated is of first importance in reducing the hazards due to radioactive contamination. For personnel, the use of respiratory protection where necessary and thorough cleansing of the hands before eating, smoking, etc., are advisable. The additional use of protective clothing, such as gloves and shoe covers, or even complete clothing changes may also provide a measure of protection.

Maintenance of Working Location

In maintaining a clean working location, adequate design of equipment in which materials are handled, with especial attention given to maintaining them in a closed system, and efficient and careful operation are prime requisites. Frequent and thorough surveys for contamination, followed by effective decontamination procedures, will aid both in maintaining an awareness of the actual cleanliness of the location and in removing such contaminating materials as do escape into the environment.

DECONTAMINATION

Definition

Decontamination may be defined as the physical removal of radioactive material from any medium. Surface contamination should be removed as a solid when possible, since use of a solvent will imbed the material in porous surfaces and make decontamination more difficult. In general, when an adequate decontaminating agent and method are used, most of the contamination is removed on the first few attempts at decontamination. Further efforts with the same decontaminating agent may result in such a small decrease in activity that it is frequently necessary to decide whether a small amount of residual contamination will be more harmful than the possible physical destruction attendant upon its removal.

Means of Decontamination

To facilitate decontamination, all working surfaces and equipment used in radiochemical operations should be nonporous and resistant to corrosion by acids, alkalies, and organic solvents. Stainless steel, as an example, is easily decontaminated and not too costly if a reasonably long-term operation is contemplated. Various acid resisting varnishes and plastics may be applied to porous surfaces in order to simplify decontamination. An absorbent paper placed on a nonporous surface will absorb most of the material accidentally spilled and prevent its distribution by air currents. Paper used as an absorber or cover should be removed and discarded as contaminated waste at frequent intervals.

Use of Protective Surface Coverings

Where area contamination presents no external hazard, as in alpha contamination, the use of paint, varnish, or plastic coating will reduce danger of ingestion, inhalation, and spread of the contaminant. It must be remembered that, even though contamination is covered, it is always present until physically removed or until it decays naturally, and natural decay can rarely be relied upon to solve the problem.

Designation of Contaminated Areas

Special systems for handling contaminated equipment should be devised. The presence of contamination should be clearly designated by appropriate marking or tags in such a manner as to assure that all persons who must come in contact with such equipment will be fully aware of its condition. Such a system will not only guard against accidental exposure but will also aid in preventing the spread of contamination to radioactively clean areas.

Restriction of Personnel and Protective Clothing and Equipment

Areas in which radiation may be encountered and in which transferable contamination is present should be clearly marked and traffic within the area limited to those persons whose job necessitates their presence.

For persons working in these areas, it may be necessary to provide adequate personal respiratory protection and special clothing which can either be disposed of or decontaminated. Rules restricting smoking, eating, application of cosmetics, etc., by persons may be required. Similarly, regulations concerning skin decontamination procedures upon leaving the area may be necessary. Adequate materials and procedures for the removal of the contaminating substances from the skin without producing damage may need to be devised.

Medical Examinations

Regular medical examinations of individuals working with radioactive materials or in locations where such materials are handled should be scheduled on an annual basis or oftener as necessary. In addition, special first-aid attention may be required for personnel receiving wounds where radioactve materials are involved.

Waste Disposal

Special attention will need to be given to the disposal of radioactive materials. In general, such disposal will probably necessitate a reduction in either the specific activity (measured in disintegrations per gram per second) of the material concerned or a reduction in its total activity. The first condition is usually obtained by diluting the waste either with a convenient material such as water or with materials including stable isotopes of the radioisotope concerned. In some instances where the waste is of comparatively small volume and much of the activity is due to short-lived radioisotopes, it may be possible to confine the waste in an impermeable tank until both its specific activity and its total activity have decreased due to radioactive decay and then dispose of it by dilution as indicated above.

Disposal of contaminated solids and liquids may usually be accomplished by burial on land (National Bureau of Standards handbooks soon to be published), or at sea in suitably weighted steel containers. This latter service is commercially available.

Air-Borne Material

If the disposal problem involves air-borne materials, tall stacks and filters will, in general, be required.

RADIATION DETECTION INSTRUMENTS

Environment Survey Types

Measure of Contamination Levels. Either portable or fixed instruments may be used for determining the radiation or contamination levels in a given location. These instruments depend for operation upon the ionization produced by the radiation and usually employ either an ionization chamber or a Geiger-Mueller tube as the detector with an appropriate indicating device.

General Purpose Instruments

Adequate portable instruments of these types are commercially available for general purpose uses. For beta-gamma detection, available instruments are capable of detecting background which is about 0.03 mr/hr in many localities. Alpha contamination of the order of 1 dis/min/cm^2 may be detected on a smooth surface. Upper limits for such detection are indefinite, depending upon the instrument, or instruments, used.

Instruments for Air Contamination

Instruments from commercial sources are available for detecting the presence of particulate radioactive material in the air.

Adequate samplers may also be obtained by adapting small vacuum pumps or air blowers so that air is drawn through a filter paper at a measured rate. The activity of the particles collected on this paper may then be measured and the concentration of the radioactive material in the air determined.

Some of the larger fixed instruments which are also available include penetrating radiation monitors, continuous air samplers, and hand and foot counters that measure the extent of contamination upon an individual's hands or shoes.

In addition to these general types of instruments, special types for particular needs, if not available, may be built to specification.

Personnel Monitoring Devices

Instruments designed to indicate the amount of radiation actually received by an employee either use small electrometers or electroscopes or use photographic-type film. The former types are the well-known dosimeters or pocket chambers that are charged at the start of the day and read at the end of the day. If they are placed in a radiation field, they will be discharged, the amount of such loss of charge being calibrated in terms of radiation received. The instruments of this type that are in general use have a usable range between approximately 10 and 200 mr, although others are available with higher ranges. In general, these instruments will measure only gamma radiation but may indicate the presence of high energy beta radiation.

Use of Personal Badges

The fact that penetrating radiation will darken photographic film makes possible the use of film placed in badges or in rings to measure personnel exposure. In general, film badges and rings are worn by personnel for periods of a week or two before being processed and the radiation exposure determined. The darkening produced is calibrated in terms of the radiation incident on the badge. Approximately 30 mr is the lowest radiation exposure that may be measured with available badges, with the upper limits being determined by the characteristics of the film used.

Personnel Monitoring

In using personnel monitoring devices, care should be taken in their handling and processing to prevent accidental exposure to radiation while they are not being worn and to prevent apparent exposure as a result of causes other than radiation.

With the possible exception of film rings, all of these items are commercially available, and at least one instrument manufacturer also provides film badge service.

RECORDS AND ROUTINE MONITORING

Maintenance of Records

Since it is considered that some injury due to radiation may be produced as the cumulative effect of many small exposures over a long period of time, and since present recommended exposure limits are below the limits where effects may be detected clinically, it is usually desirable to maintain rather complete records both of personnel exposure as shown by personnel monitoring devices and of environmental conditions as shown by routine monitoring.

Nature of Records

Obviously, personnel exposure records will include such medical data obtained by blood counts, urinalysis, etc., as the physician concerned will consider necessary. In addition, information concerning actual personnel exposure as indicated by film badges, dosimeters or pocket chambers, and film rings should be maintained. It may also be desirable to maintain such indirect evidence of possible radiation exposure as that indicated by the results of air samples taken near the employee's work location and the readings shown by the routine hand monitoring or clothing monitoring programs if these are used. Records of these types where established limits are exceeded should be maintained on the same basis as the direct personnel exposure data. It may also be considered advisable to maintain for at least a period of time the results of routine area and job monitoring. At this time, it appears that limits for some of these conditions, such as those involving surface alpha contamination, may need to be established by the laboratory itself.

Frequency of Monitoring

The frequency and extent of actual routine monitoring in any location will depend upon the conditions anticipated. Thus, if there is a possibility of continuous slight air contamination in the work location, shift-length air sampling is indicated; otherwise, spot audits at irregular intervals will supply the necessary information. In most locations where radioactive materials are handled, employees should check their hands for possible radioactive contamination at least at the end of the shift and before eating. Protective clothing should be checked before wearing, especially if beta-gamma emitting contamination is possible. Where penetrating radiation is a problem, thorough beta-gamma checks of the work location and routine contamination monitoring should be made periodically, possibly once each week, or even each shift if the hazard potentiality warrants it.

Environmental Monitoring

In addition to these routine monitoring activities, additional monitoring is advisable when major environmental changes occur. These could be caused by operational variations involving equipment changes in the vicinity of an active source, changes in shielding, releases or spills of radioactive materials, special jobs, or other conditions where changes in radiation intensity or contamination spread appear possible.

Responsibility of Supervision and Personnel

In general, it should be the responsibility of supervision, and the workers themselves, to do their own monitoring as a part of the job. Under these conditions, the employees themselves may become interested in determining the steps which should be taken to correct faults in their own contamination control methods. A rather complete program of education of employees in general

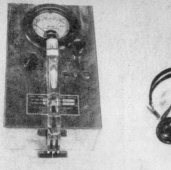

JUNO - ALPHA, BETA & GAMMA SURVEY METER

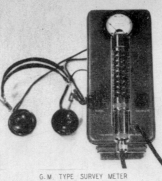

G. M. TYPE SURVEY METER

SAMSON - ALPHA SURVEY METER

CUTIE PIE - GAMMA SURVEY METER

FILM BADGE & FILM RING

POCKET CHAMBERS & CHARGER REA

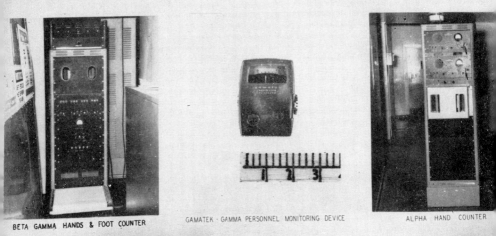

BETA GAMMA HANDS & FOOT COUNTER

GAMATEK - GAMMA PERSONNEL MONITORING DEVICE

ALPHA HAND COUNTER

Union Carbide & Carbon Corp.

Plate 27. Examples of various radiation survey and monitoring instruments. The inclusion or exclusion of specific instruments does not necessarily endorse or disapprove their use.

radiation information as well as in the specific radiation aspects of their jobs is indicated as a very desirable program in all plants where such radiation is encountered.

SUMMARY

From the foregoing, it may be concluded that an adequate program for the control of radiation hazards involves the following considerations:

1. Adequate design of equipment and facilities, including shielding where necessary and provisions to prevent the spreading of radioactive material.

2. Well-considered operating procedures designed to prevent not only the routine exposure of personnel to excessive radiation but also the spreading of radioactive materials. These should include procedures to be used in case of an accident involving the possibility of personnel exposure.

3. Education of personnel concerned with the problems of radiation and their solution.

4. Monitoring of personnel for contamination and radiation exposure, including annual medical examinations.

5. Routine monitoring of areas and air if the radioactive material used is in such form that it can be distributed.

6. Thorough decontamination of personnel and areas where necessary.

7. Proper maintenance of radiation detecting instruments and devices, including routine checks of their calibration.

8. Adequate records, especially of personnel exposure to conditions exceeding established limits.

CHAPTER X

Pressure Vessel Hazards

Chemists and laboratory technicians should not allow their enthusiasm for some research problem to blind them to good principles of equipment selection in choosing pressure vessels for a given project. Design safety factors should not be ignored or misinterpreted just because such projects are usually temporary in nature. The maximum working pressure with coincident temperature, or the maximum working temperature with coincident pressure, should be determined for each pressure vessel to be used, and these pressure-temperature ratings should not be exceeded in service.

All types of laboratory pressure vessels and auxiliary equipment require careful selection, inspection, and testing; and ample time should be given to development of safe methods of handling such equipment, including pilot plant work and semi-plant operations as well as laboratory work.

Many systems are used in the laboratory to help control pressure vessel hazards. Whatever the system, it should be coupled with an effective educational program, reaching all personnel involved in pressure vessel work. Every effort should be made to assure a clear understanding of possible hazards involved.

Whenever possible, a file should be set up for every vessel before it goes into service. This should contain a print of the vessel along with all revisions, the fabrication record, a record of fabrication inspections, a certificate of fabrication compliance with design requirements, and specific information as to maximum allowable working pressure, maximum allowable working temperature, construction materials, lining material, special alloys, and pressure relief equipment. This file should contain all subsequent information on periodic tests and inspection data.

A service log history should be maintained on each vessel, whether it sees service in one type of experiment or process or many. This is necessary because each application introduces different corrosion factors.

Chemical laboratories connected with pilot-scale operations usually come under routine inspection and test schedules. Special personnel are maintained within, or are directly controlled by, the engineering staff of most organizations. The primary purpose of such inspection groups is to assure the safe operation of pressure vessels and to provide for maintenance and repair during shutdown periods, as well as to determine vessel-use expectancy and required replacement. The majority of tests and inspections are based on procedures outlined in the latest editions of the ASME [1] and API ASME [2] code books. Thickness determinations and other vessel properties may be ascertained with a variety of instruments and the allowable operating pressure calculated by formulas outlined in these code books. The average laboratory, lacking such facilities, may readily establish its own testing and inspection program involving the simpler but time-proven methods adequately described in these codes.

Safety Devices

Interchangeable or permanent safety devices should be available for equipment set-ups and should include rupture disks, and spring-loaded relief valves of the pop type for gas or vapor service, and nonpop type for liquid service. Multiple vessels which are interconnected without block valves may be equipped with a single safety device, provided all pressure relieving requirements of the ASME or API-ASME codes are fulfilled.

Rupture disks should be of special design when installed on pressure vessels which inadvertently or intentionally may be sub-

---

[1] American Society of Mechanical Engineers, Section VIII, Unfired Pressure Vessels, of the ASME Boiler and Pressure Vessel Code.

[2] American Petroleum Institute and the American Society of Mechanical Engineers, *Unfired Pressure Vessels for Petroleum Liquids and Gases.*

Plate 28. A typical control panel installation of a high-pressure building. Behind the panel can be seen, at the door entrance, an 8-inch reinforced concrete wall with a pneumatically operated steel door. Above the control panels are two exhaust hoods that are operated separately with explosion-proof fans on each. All excess hydrogen and other volatiles are exhausted through these hoods.

jected to vacuum pressure, or the installation of a vacuum relief valve should be considered.

Proper combinations of rupture disks and relief valves may be used in those cases where material coming in contact with the valve can interfere with its action.

Where disk rupture would lead to loss of all the product, relief valves should be used alone or in unit combination with rupture disks. In no case shall a combination rupture disk and relief-valve installation be made without provision of a pressure gauge, try cock, or free vent on the connection between the rupture disk and relief-valve to determine that back pressure has not built up within this connection.

Descriptive data and general application recommendations are readily available from most valve manufacturers.[3] Recommended installation procedures are outlined in the ASME and API-ASME Codes. All relief valves and rupture disks should be legibly marked with the relieving pressure. Test the relief valves for conformance before installation.

Only approved replacement material should be used for rupture disks.

Relief lines should be of ample size to prevent back pressure on the valve and should be vented to the outside atmosphere at a high point of the building or structure. This is particularly important when working with a flammable or toxic material. Where several relief valves discharge into a single header, the header shall be of ample size to prevent back pressure interfering with the proper operation of other connected valves. Relief lines should be provided with a drain opening to prevent accumulation of condensate.

Relief valves and rupture disks should not be valved off at any time. Multiple relief valves or multiple rupture disks must be equipped with interlocking simultaneously acting valves so that the vessel will always be open to pressure relief.

It is recommended that competent engineers and operating men review and approve all new projects that require use of a

[3] Farris Engineering Company, Palisades Park, New Jersey; Crane Company, Chicago, Illinois; Black, Sivalls and Bryson, Kansas City, Missouri; and others.

pressure vessel. In a small laboratory, the supervisor should assume responsibility for this.

Cylinders

Safe Load. A specific volume, pressure, and temperature diagram should be used for loading all material where such safe loads have not already been established. Such a diagram can be prepared by actual measurement, as described by Sage and Lacey,[4] and others. A diagram may also be derived by methods described by Hougen and Watson.[5] Overloading can lead to rupture if the cylinder is stored in a warm area or exposed to the sun's rays.

Fusible Plugs. Such plugs are useful safety devices for cylinders that may be exposed to fire or other sources of heat. When it gets warm, the plug melts, releasing the contents without rupturing the cylinder. Since soft plugs usually melt below live steam temperature, it is recommended that the plugs be removed if live steam is to be used in cleaning the cylinder. The plugs must be re-installed before reloading the cylinder.

Polymerization. Extreme caution must be exercised with any material which may polymerize in a cylinder. Should polymerization start, the cylinder must be carefully watched and its pressure controlled. Normally 100°F is considered the maximum temperature found in laboratory storage areas. Outdoors in direct sunlight, skin temperatures of cylinders may reach 130°F. When a material polymerizes, these temperatures may be greatly exceeded, and the resulting pressure may burst the cylinder.

Valves. All loading and discharge valve designs should provide for capping the valve to prevent damage to the valve due to mishandling.

Labels. All cylinders should be properly labeled at all times with shoulder marking tags or other prescribed identification that will withstand weathering.

Maintenance. Cylinders containing highly corrosive materials should be inspected for small leaks around valves. Such leaks may

[4] Sage and Lacey, *Industrial and Engineering Chemistry,* various dates.
[5] *Chemical Process Principles—Part II,* Hougen and Watson.

cause the valve parts to stick or fail and present a hazard on release.

Bombs

Glass Bombs and Block Type Furnaces. In handling bombs in laboratory and pilot plant work, it is desirable to start preliminary work with minimum quantities to determine approximate pressures and hazards which may develop. A convenient procedure is to build small, block type, metallic furnaces. Steel protective bombs with screw caps, carrying small sealed glass bombs, are appropriate. The small glass bomb permits the research worker to start with material quantities of 5 cc or less. Attained pressure, bomb breakage, and other preliminary information about the reaction may be thus obtained.

The block type furnace serves as the heating and control medium, and the metallic protection over the glass gives additional protection to personnel. This method of approach may disclose operational hazards before larger batch-type operations are contemplated.

Bombs with an inside diameter larger than 6 inches that will be used in services at 15 psi or higher shall be considered as pressure vessels and shall be designed in conformance with the ASME Unfired Pressure Vessel Code. The wall thickness of bombs with an inside diameter of 6 inches or less for any pressure may be determined by the formulas shown in the latest edition of ASA B31.1, American Standard Code for Pressure Piping.

Supervision should make available a specific volume-pressure temperature diagram.[6] Such a diagram will permit a determination of the proper volume load for the bomb and may indicate in advance whether the reaction will proceed as anticipated, or whether the bomb may break due to liquid expansion or gas pressure.

Exercise care in both loading and unloading bombs. Extra precautions should be taken in the unloading cycle to assure that

[6] Method of calculation described by Hougen and Watson, Sage and Lacey, and others.

heads and other connections are loosened and that no crystalline deposit or foreign matter is preventing release of pressure. Bombs in which reactions are taking place should be placed in safety shelters and away from routine activities of the laboratory.

Bomb Shelters. Many university and industrial laboratories use some type of enclosure for bomb work. Essentially they are designed to confine and direct the force of possible explosions away from personnel.

These shelters, in many cases, will consist of two layers of $\frac{1}{2}$-inch boiler or armor plate, spaced approximately 2 inches apart. Bombs are placed inside this structure and the control or recording instruments are located away from it. Shelter sizes will vary.

Another type of construction, which has been equally well accepted, consists of a single layer of 1-inch boiler or armor plate.

Still another type of construction, for work involving extremely high pressures, consists of heavy concrete walls, built into the sides of hills.

Whenever bombs are used, the operator should determine the nature of anticipated hazards and provide necessary protection in advance.

Reactors

Polymerizers. Polymerizers have come into extensive use in the past decade and, in many cases, offer specific operational hazards. Polymer may collect on the sides of the unit, safety lines, bearings, around pumps and other locations, with a resultant stoppage of the mixing action, a shut-off of the vacuum lines, and a blocking of the safety vents and reliefs.

Extreme care should be taken to determine the points at which the polymer may deposit. In batch kettles and sometimes in continuous kettles, the material may reach the vapor phase, polymerize, collect on the sides of reactor, and plug the safety lines.

In most agitated mass polymerizations, laboratory personnel should bear in mind that, as the concentration of a polymer increases, viscosity also increases; thus mixing becomes increasingly difficult and the heat removal seriously delayed. Poor mixing

Plate 29. A 5-gallon batch-type autoclave capable of withstanding, and operating at, 2000 psi. In this photograph one can see the reinforced concrete walls and the blowout panel directly behind the autoclave. It will also be noted that there is an explosion-proof fan operating at all times in the upper portion of this panel. Close inspection of the ceiling structure will also reveal the blowout hatches directly over the autoclave. Should anything happen in this room, the roof and the panel would release any excessive pressure that might be placed on the reinforced concrete wall protecting the personnel.

may cause an uneven temperature rise and the over-all reaction rate may be increased tremendously. Adequate cooling is therefore essential.

Batch Autoclaves. In working with batch autoclaves, the operator should make sure that the design pressure is adequate for the maximum contemplated operating pressure. Safeguards against fire should also be provided. Safety devices should be checked for proper size and set pressure. Vent outlets should be located where fumes will not be carried into adjacent work areas or picked up by air-conditioning inlets. Material purging must be carried to the outside atmosphere or to blow-down drums and not released into the room where people may be working.

Alkylators. The alkylator represents another type of reactor used in laboratories, pilot plants, and semi-plants. Explosion and fire are primary hazards associated with gases and alkylating agents in this equipment. Careful inspection is required to assure that corrosion, erosion, or leaks do not allow the materials to vent or spill into the working area. Acids or acid-forming materials are usually involved in this type of reaction; hence, special precautions should be taken to prevent water entering the system and causing corrosion of the alkylator itself.

Alkylators are usually large in size and should be adequately diked. Fire walls should surround the unit if it is larger than 5 gallons. Provide steam snuffer or CO_2 systems to control fires.

Devolatilizers. Devolatilizers or stripping coils used on high boiling materials, for the most part, present hazards similar to those common to polymerizer units. Precautions must be taken to ascertain that material will not accumulate at critical locations and that the safety vent lines are in operating condition at all times.

Coil Reactors. An advantage of the coil type reactor in pilot plant or laboratory applications is its ability to hold only small quantities of material, thus permitting the reaction to be carried out with maximum safety. It would be redundant to discuss all types of equipment that properly fall in this category, but there are general hazards common to most of them, and ways to minimize such hazards that are worthy of mention:

1. Before putting a coil in service, it is essential to know the allowable working pressure it will stand. The corrosion factor and its effect on the coil should be considered.

2. Similarly the upper and lower temperature limitation of the coil materials should be determined. Much coil plugging can be avoided by selective design that makes proper allowance for expected operating temperatures.

Operating temperatures must remain uppermost in the mind of both designer and operator because carbon steels are suitable only within a certain temperature range. Above 850°F they have limited resistance to oxidation, and for temperatures below minus 20°F, other materials, such as copper or various types of stainless steels, are recommended. To be considered, also, are such reactants as sulfur, chlorine, and other similar materials which cause accelerated corrosion as the temperature increases.

3. Materials recommended for specific use are described in the Material Specifications Section of the ASME Boiler and Pressure Vessel Code, and that source should be consulted.

Kettles. Kettles (other than Pfaudler type) are frequently used in both laboratory and pilot plant operations. The hazards involved are similar to large volume equipment. Primary attention should be directed to controlling reaction run-aways. There should be on hand the means to control potential fires in case the contents of the kettle get out of control and spill out of the kettle.

Vaporizers. This class of equipment used frequently in pilot plant units presents specific hazards. The vaporizing material may have a tendency to deposit carbon in varying thicknesses on the interior surfaces, with a consequent lowering of the heat transfer rate. This may lead to local overheating on the surface of the vessel, permitting corrosion to occur, or may spill the contents of the vaporizer into the work area. This hazard should be guarded against by providing a maximum amount of protection for the operating personnel.

Boilers

High-temperature operations, where steam cannot be used, may require a special heat transfer medium.

Electric Heaters. Electric heaters are common pieces of laboratory equipment. Care should be exercised to prevent materials from spilling on the electrical parts and terminals. Heaters in operation should be fully immersed in the material to be heated. When a pump is used to circulate liquid over a heater, the velocity should be sufficient to avoid excessively high temperature and accompanying carbon formation as the liquid decomposes.

Direct Fired Boilers. This type of equipment may find only occasional usage. Heat transfer media other than water are employed and, accordingly, suitable precautions against possible fires should be taken and personnel protective equipment should be provided.

Solids Heaters. Major concern in operating solids heaters is assuring continuous flow of material through the tubes or heaters in service. Hazards are comparable to those associated with vaporizers and, whenever material stoppage occurs within a tube or reactor, the heat transfer surface becomes readily overheated with subsequent danger from oxidation of the metal, corrosion, and even melting.

Superheaters. Steam, hydrocarbon, and various types of gas superheaters require extreme care in the design stage so that the proper type of metal may be selected for fabrication. This should be determined from the nature of the service to which the superheater will be put. In operation, the skin temperature of the metal must be accurately measured and the heater's temperature controlled to prevent its overheating and possible rupture.

Reboilers. The so-called reboilers used in a laboratory can be designed and fabricated from a corrosion-resistant material suitable for the service.

Reboilers may be operated with high-pressure steam. A major hazard can and does occur when ruptured tubes in the reboiler permit steam to enter the still, reactor, or other equipment in which the reboiler is installed. The maximum pressure occurring in a reboiler will determine the required design pressure, relief equipment, and venting on the enclosing vessel.

Cause of such rupture may be the reaction occurring when steam or water is admitted to a highly corrosive mixture.

Heat Exchangers. While design factors of both high- and low-temperature heat exchangers are controlled by various standard methods employed by the fabricator, metal for their construction should be selected on the basis of their intended application. Design should provide for proper expansion and contraction. Proper means of relief should be provided if plug solidification or freeze-up occurs. The heat exchanger should be designed to be quickly dismantled when cleaning is necessary.

Condensers. Condensers are subject to the same design considerations as heat exchangers. In application, however, particularly on high temperature equipment, their operation may be controlled by what is known as the two-valve system—i.e., one valve is installed on the vent line of the condenser, another valve in the outgoing water line. The pressure controller can then set the valve on the water line to operate between the limits of zero and 7 pounds. Seven pounds is the setting for the wide-open valve when the maximum amount of coolant used is between 7 and 14 pounds. The valve on the vent line may be opened to permit the pressure to be relieved on the compressors, blow-down drums, or gas holders. This arrangement is not intended to preclude the installation of required pop-type relief valves and rupture disk safety installations.

Refrigeration Equipment

Procedure has been standardized, and adequate information is readily available for proper design of refrigeration equipment. In putting such equipment to use, however, there may be a hazard involving the material to be refrigerated. A check should be made to ensure that no reaction can occur should a leak develop. Examples of reactions that would occur are those involving use of an ammonia system on a hydrochloric acid condenser, and a chlorine refrigerant on an alkyl benzene or paraffin hydrocarbon condenser.

Storage Tanks—Atmospheric Pressure Type

All tanks used in conjunction with laboratory equipment for the receiving or storing of materials should conform to these basic requirements:

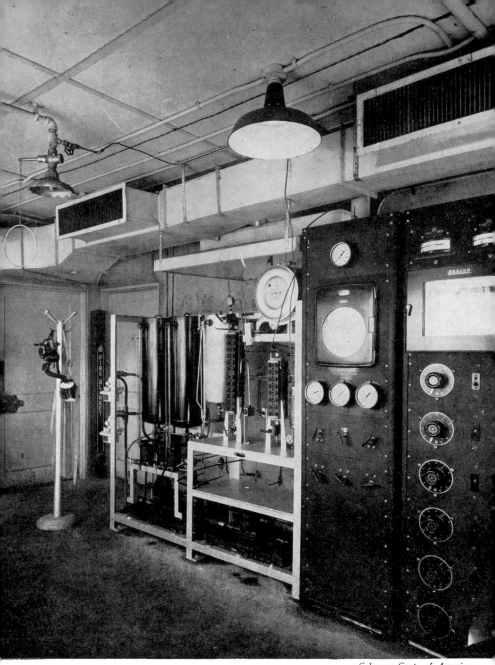

Celanese Corp. of America

Plate 30. The main control room in a high-pressure building for the operation of a continuous hydrogenation reaction. Note the reactors, which are in a separate stall behind a reinforced concrete wall behind this equipment. It will also be noted that additional safety equipment, such as fire blankets, gas masks, aprons, safety showers, is available in this room, and that adequate ventilation is supplied through the ducts in the top portion of the picture.

E. I. du Pont de Nemours & Co., Inc.

Plate 31. A corner of a Special Service Laboratory in which a range of research equipment is available. Chemical reactions and various physical operations can be carried out here that would not ordinarily be possible in a conventional research laboratory.

Celanese Corp. of America

Plate 32. A group of buildings into which hazardous operations have been moved. The large section on the right is the high-pressure hydrogenation laboratory. The interior walls between the operator and operation are made of reinforced concrete in order to protect the operator. The roof is made up of sections which are easily removed and which would blow free in the case of an explosion. The back section of each explosive or hazardous bay is covered with a plastic screen that is pinned in place for easy removal. Behind this is a heavy sand barrier similar to those used in many powder plants operated by the Army and Navy. In the center of the picture is a small building which is classified as the hazardous gas laboratory. This building has been especially designed with the proper scrubbers for the removal of toxic gases. The building in the left rear of the picture is a small unit specially designed for ether extraction work. Exterior ventilation is provided at all times, and exhaust fans remove the heavy vapors from benches and floors at all points where the ether may escape into the room. All of these installations, the high-pressure building, the hazardous gas laboratory, and the ether extraction building, are of Class I, Group D. Floors are spark-proof and ground wires are imbedded in them.

Plate 33. An orderly pilot plant laboratory in which minute details are being worked out with regard to selection of most suitable equipment, yields, and quality of intermediate and end products.

1. Design and fabrication shall conform to API Standard 12-C, for welded storage tanks, whenever applicable.

2. Small-sized storage tanks may be designed and fabricated to conform to the Underwriters' Laboratories Standard for Above Ground Storage Tanks for Flammable Liquids.

3. Open vents shall be used only on tanks containing non-flammable materials.

4. Pressure-vacuum relief valves shall be sized to handle the capacity recommended in API publication RP-2000, "Guide for Tank Venting." Materials of construction for relief valves shall be selected to resist corrosion and to prevent valve pallet sticking to valve seat.

Plate 34. Another view of a pilot plant laboratory in which process development is conducted and control testing is underway.

5. Automatic sprinkling should be provided if necessary.

6. Outside tanks used for storage of flammable liquids should be properly located as recommended by National Fire Protection Association Pamphlet No. 30.

7. Dikes should be provided on large outside storage tanks of flammable or combustible liquids. They should be sized and constructed as recommended by National Fire Protection Association Pamphlet No. 30.

8. Tank connections should be well braced.

9. Valves and gauge glasses must be located and protected so that they cannot be knocked off by passing trucks or climbing men.

10. Hot material should be pumped with caution into a storage tank, because vents may become plugged and the tank collapse because of the vacuum developed by the subsequent cooling of the material.

11. Pressure-vacuum relief valves should be dismantled and inspected at frequent intervals. It is suggested that inspection of these valves be made at intervals not exceeding 30 days.

12. When air is admitted to a tank, corrosion may result, and it may be desirable with certain materials to provide an inert gas blanketing system in addition to the pressure-vacuum relief valves normally required.

Manhole Requirements

All vessels which must be entered for servicing should have at least one 22-inch minimum diameter manhole for safe entry. If vessel size or design preclude the possibility of meeting this speci- fication, the vessel should be provided with a hand-hole, 10-inch maximum diameter size.

CHAPTER XI

Clothing and Personal Protective Equipment

Chemical laboratories should have special protective clothing and equipment readily available for emergency use and for secondary protection for personnel working with hazardous materials.

Protective equipment, however, should not be relied on when safer methods can be employed. At best, protective equipment provides only limited protection, and unless everyone in a laboratory is so equipped, others are endangered by unsafe apparatus and equipment set-ups.

The quantity and type of clothing and protective equipment that a laboratory should have available will depend on its size and the type of work carried on in it. In practically every chemical laboratory there is a possible danger of toxic gases being released and, therefore, a need for masks to protect those who may have to enter the laboratory when such emergencies arise.

Laboratory work is varied and usually involves corrosive chemicals and fragile glass apparatus; hence, there is the possibility of serious eye injuries. In many industrial and academic chemical laboratories, all personnel are required to wear safety glasses at all times. Where a significant fire hazard exists, it may be advisable to provide special fire-retardant garments or even chrome leather clothing and hoods for more complete protection.

It is important that the laboratory personnel be thoroughly familiar with the emergency equipment available, its location, manner of use, and, especially, its limitations. Emergency equipment should be located in places readily accessible but not neces-

Gen. Chemical Div., Allied Chemical & Dye Corp.

Plate 35. Suitable protective clothing and safeguards incorporated in the equipment in which radioactive measurements are underway. Note the shielding above the control panel.

sarily next to the location where potentially dangerous work is performed.

Many laboratories have found that the best location for emergency equipment is near exits which workers are likely to use in an emergency.

It is also essential that all personal protective equipment be inspected, cleaned, and sterilized at regular intervals and always before use by another person.

Eye Protection

Eye protection is of paramount importance, and experience indicates that workers should always wear suitable safety glasses when in the laboratory. There are many styles and types of safety glasses available. Some types may be had with corrective lenses. The following are representative of the principal styles which have been found satisfactory for laboratory use.

1. Metal-rimmed safety spectacles with specially hardened glass or plastic lenses, available with or without side shields.

2. Plastic-rimmed safety spectacles with hardened glass or plastic lenses, available with or without side shields.

3. The all-plastic monotype safety goggle, which ordinarily can be worn over corrective glasses.

4. The rubber-framed goggle with plastic or hardened glass lenses. This type offers more complete eye protection than the types previously mentioned.

5. Cup-type safety goggles with glass or plastic lens, available in several styles, some of which are suitable for wearing over corrective glasses.

6. Nitrometer masks for use where complete face protection is required.

7. Plastic face shields which may be worn over the spectacle type safety glass for additional face protection.

Properly fitted safety glasses are comfortable and offer adequate protection for most routine laboratory work. It is desirable, however, when doing work known to be potentially dangerous to the eyes, to wear more complete eye protection, such as is offered by chemical goggles and/or plastic face shields. Proper care of safety glasses follows:

1. The lens must be kept clean. A dirty lens obscures vision and may lead to eye fatigue. The lens should be regularly cleaned with soap and water—but never with abrasive-type hand soaps, since they will scratch the lens. When cleaning safety glasses that have plastic lenses, any abrasive dirt which may be on the surface should always be washed off by holding the glasses under a running water tap for a moment. Unless this is done the lens will become scratched from abrasive matter being rubbed on the lens.

2. Safety glasses should never be left in a position where the lens is in contact with hard surfaces, such as table tops.

3. Safety glasses should not be carried in the same pocket with other objects, such as pencils, files, etc. It is good practice to keep the glasses in a case when they are not being worn.

Body Protection

Laboratory coats, overalls, aprons, smocks, and similar garments should be made available for protection of the body and clothes from corrosive chemicals. Some of the garments currently available are highly resistant to many corrosive chemicals, and, in addition, some also have excellent flame-retardant qualities. Since none of the garments possess all of the qualities that may be desired, it will be necessary to select clothing made out of the material which will be most resistant to the chemicals generally handled in the laboratory.

The following general types of flameproof clothing are available:

1. Temporary flame-retardant treatments which can be applied to regular clothing but must be re-applied after each laundering, since they are generally water soluble.

2. Permanent-type, flame-retardant agents which must be applied to the mill goods before garments are fabricated. The treatment will withstand as many as twenty-five commercial launderings.

3. Various new synthetic materials that are flame-retardant as

Plate 36. Flame-resistant garments, including head protection. Breathing
apparatus resting on ledge.

well as being highly resistant to the attack of many solvents, acids, and certain other chemicals. Garments of this type, unless treated with anti-static compounds, have been found to generate static electricity; therefore, their use in working with flammables may increase the danger of fire.

Aprons made of solvent-proof plastics, oil-resisting synthetic rubber, or other suitable protective material, should be available for use when laboratory personnel frequently handle hazardous chemicals.

CAUTION—Some of these materials also generate static electricity.

Complete suits or a combination smock and air-line mask should be provided for personnel exposed to high atmospheric concentrations of corrosive chemicals or dusty materials.

Chrome leather garments, including pants, coat, hood, gloves, and spats, should be worn by personnel exposed to considerable heat.

Respiratory Protection

Respiratory protective equipment is of two general types. One is a device commonly called a respirator, which removes dust and solid particles from inhaled air. The other type is designed to remove harmful gases from air being drawn into the respiratory tract.

There are many different styles of respirators on the market, and some are designed to accommodate different types of filters and cartridges which offer protection against specific hazards. The U. S. Bureau of Mines approves certain types of filters and classifies them as follows:

Type A respirator is equipped with a filter approved for protection against silica and nuisance dusts.

Type B respirator is equipped with a finer filter than Type A and is approved for protection against toxic dusts and some metal fumes.

Metal Fumes respirators, which have especially treated filters, will offer protection against most metal fumes, such as iron, zinc, cadmium, and chromium. Such respirators, however,

Plate 37. Respiratory protective equipment used by repair worker about to enter a tank. Note attendant holding life-line. At least one man must remain outside the tank for any emergency that might arise.

Celanese Corp. of America

only remove solids from the air and do not absorb gases. For example, these respirators will not give protection against metals in a true gaseous state, such as mercury.

Chemical Cartridge respirators are equipped with replaceable cartridges that contain gas-absorbing material. These may be used to avoid inhaling disagreeable but harmless concentrations of obnoxious vapors. They are not recommended for protection where toxic quantities of an air contaminant may be encountered.

The principal precautions to remember when using dust respirators is that they do not offer protection against harmful gases. Even the chemical cartridge respirator is not recommended for use where dangerous concentrations of gas may be present.

Filters must be changed at varying intervals depending on the concentrations of dust encountered or when the resistance to breathing increases to a point of discomfort. When respirators are used regularly they should be cleaned and sterilized as necessary, but at least weekly, and always before use by another person.

Gas masks, however, offer protection against toxic gases and dusts. The canister-type masks offer limited protection, since they depend on a gas-absorbing material to remove contaminants from the air or merely purify the inhaled air. They do not offer protection against possible oxygen deficiency (below 16% by volume) in air, such as may be encountered when entering tanks or other confined spaces. Their use is also not recommended when concentrations of a toxic gas in excess of 2% by volume (for ammonia, 3%) may be encountered.

Canister-type masks are equipped with various absorbing agents offering protection against specific gas or gases. The life of a canister varies depending on its use and the concentrations encountered. The following table lists the principal types of canisters, the absorbent they contain, and the protection they will provide:

Color	Filtering Material	Protection
Black	Activated charcoal	Organic vapors
White	Soda lime or sodium hydroxide fused on pumice	Acid gases
Yellow	Activated charcoal and soda lime	Acid gases and organic vapors
Yellow with Black Stripes	Activated charcoal and soda lime and cloth filter	Acid gases, organic vapors, dusts, smoke, and mists
Green	Silica gel	Ammonia
Brown	Silica gel, activated charcoal, soda lime	Acid gases, organic vapors, and ammonia
Red	Activated charcoal, silica gel, sodium hydroxide fused on pumice, Hopcalite, and cloth filter	The majority of gases, vapors, and fumes, including carbon monoxide

Note: When carbon monoxide may be encountered, the red canister should be used with the approved mask equipped with a timing device, since the gas is odorless.

Canister gas masks have been widely used for emergency purposes and for protection and routine service work, but, because of their limitations, many laboratories are installing the more reliable self-contained types of breathing apparatus. A person's sense of smell is the only test for a canister-type mask, but it must be remembered that most toxic gases, although their odor is pronounced at first, soon affect the sense of smell and become barely noticeable. It is important, therefore, that a person wearing a canister-type mask leave the area immediately upon detecting the odor of any gas. It may mean that the concentration of the gas encountered is too high, the face piece is not properly adjusted and is leaking, the canister is no longer serviceable, or the mask is equipped with the wrong type of canister.

Self-contained types of masks are much safer and more comfortable, since the wearer carries either a supply of air or an oxygen generator, and this type does not depend on purification of contaminated air for breathing purposes. The two types most widely employed require training in their use:

Compressed Air Masks fitted with the demand type valve releases compressed air in the cylinder automatically as required by the wearer. The mask is equipped with a cylinder containing as much as one hour's supply of air, which is usually carried on the wearer's back. This type of mask is also available with a smaller cylinder, containing about a 15-minute supply of air, which is carried by a sling and can be put on quickly. Although compressed air type masks are relatively foolproof, the wearer must carry a rather heavy cylinder.

Chemical Oxygen-Producing Mask is well suited for emergency and service use. This type of mask is equipped with a special canister that absorbs the exhaled carbon dioxide and generates oxygen. This mask is lighter than the compressed air type, but it is bulky, and once the seal is broken on the canister, it must be discarded. The canister, under ordinary usage, can supply sufficient oxygen for 1 hour.

Air-line masks obtain their air supply through a hose from a remote source, such as the laboratory air supply, and often can be used to advantage in nonemergency operations. These devices are available with either a half-mask or full-mask face piece. They are usually equipped with a flexible or corrugated air supply hose, connecting the face piece to a control valve which is worn on the belt. The control valve permits the wearer to adjust the air to the desired amount for comfort.

Extreme care should be exercised in obtaining a safe air supply. Air from a large reciprocating type compressor often contains harmful gases from the decomposition of the lubricating oils used. It is preferable to obtain the air supply from externally lubricated blowers. It is also important that blower or air source be in an area which is free from air contaminants. Line filters containing activated charcoal may be used to advantage to remove moisture and certain other contaminants.

It is hazardous to supply compressed air directly to a mask or respirator if the pressure exceeds 25 lb per square inch. Therefore, if air is obtained from a general laboratory source, a pressure reducer or regulator should be installed near the point where the air line is attached to the compressed air supply. As a further precaution, the Bureau of Mines recommends that a relief or pop-off valve be installed, pre-set to release at a pressure slightly above 25 lb per square inch.

Since air-line masks depend on a remote air supply, they should be used only where conditions will permit safe escape in the event that air supply fails.

Cleaning and Servicing

Cleaning and servicing personal protective equipment is vital to safety. Since it is of a personal nature, such equipment should be cleaned and sterilized before use by another person and should be kept clean and in good repair at all times so that it will give maximum efficiency. Where personal protective equipment is being used to protect against chemicals that may cause sensitization, it is particularly important that they be kept scrupulously clean at all times.

In general, such equipment may be scrubbed with soap and lukewarm water. Sterilizing methods employed will depend on the nature of the equipment. Ordinarily, face pieces and other items made of rubber will not withstand temperatures sufficiently high for sterilization. There are, however, a number of synthetic detergents on the market, such as those used for sterilizing glassware in restaurants, which are satisfactory for cleaning and sterilizing personal protective equipment.

Foot Protection

Leather or rubber safety shoes with built in steel toe caps are recommended where heavy objects are customarily handled or there are other foot hazards. Leather safety shoes should prove satisfactory for general wear, but rubber safety shoes are recommended where there is a considerable amount of water, acid, or other chemicals present on the floors. Rubbers may be worn over leather safety shoes.

Where there may be explosive atmospheres as a result of either flammable vapors or gases in the air, it is recommended that the hazard of static electricity be mitigated by the use of safety shoes constructed without metal and with conductive soles. However,

Plate 38. Method of handling dry ice. Note hand protection and the container constructed of heavy padded canvas. This type of container serves a dual purpose in that it reduces loss from evaporation and confines the breaking of the dry ice cake to a small protected area.

Esso Research Center, Standard Oil Development Co.

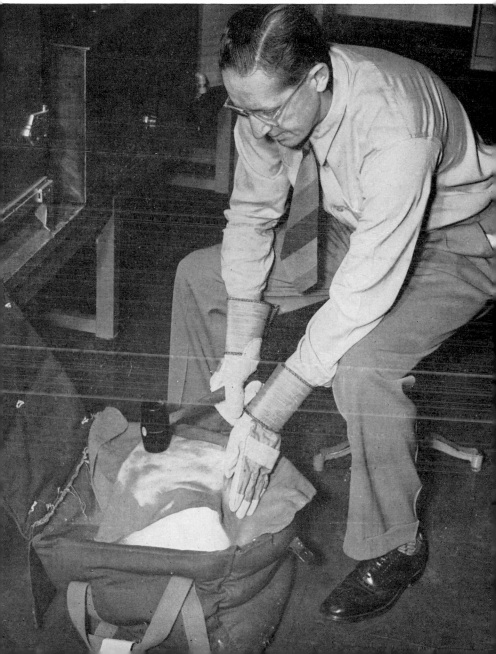

unless a conductive floor is installed in the laboratory, static charges will not be dissipated as they are generated.

Hand Protection

Many minor or first-aid injuries in laboratories may be prevented by the proper utilization of effective hand protection. A variety of gloves are available:

1. Knit cotton gloves, which are available in wrist length and gauntlet style, afford protection for general handling of abrasives, etc., and particularly glassware.

2. These knit cotton gloves are also available dipped in various materials, including rubber, synthetic rubber which is particularly oil-resistant, and various plastics which are quite resistant to solvents.

3. Where hand protection is desirable but finger dexterity is essential, a surgeon's type of glove of either natural rubber or various synthetic rubbers may be used. One type has roughened surfaces to make it particularly suitable for handling wet glassware safely.

4. Heavy rubber gloves available in different sizes up to elbow length are recommended for handling concentrated acids or other corrosives. These are especially recommended for glassware washers using chromic acid cleaning solution.

5. Fleece-lined asbestos gloves should be available to all personnel who must handle hot objects.

CHAPTER XII

Laboratory First Aid and Suggestions for Medical Treatment[1]

Hazards common to chemical laboratories call for somewhat specialized phases of first aid, and it is with these that this discussion deals. General directions for first aid are not included and can best be found in such a source as the *Textbook on First Aid* of the American Red Cross.

Burns, eye injuries, and poisoning are the injuries with which laboratory people must be most concerned. First emphasis in the laboratory, as in any place where dangerous materials are handled, should be on preventing accidents. This means observing all recognized safe practices, using necessary personal protective equipment, and exercising proper control over poisonous substances at the source of exposure.

In first aid and subsequent treatment, there are very few short cuts by way of an "antidote." Chemical antidotes are usually to be avoided, since body tissues are poor test tubes for reactions which may result from their use. One's first thought should be to remove the victim from contact with the material—not "neutralization." A few well recognized specific treatments, used only under the direction of a physician, are given at the end of this chapter.

It should be definitely understood that this section contains considerable material not intended as a guide for first-aid attendants, but, as indicated in the text, given as suggestions for medical

---

[1] The material in this chapter was prepared by the Medical Advisory Committee of the Manufacturing Chemists' Association, Inc.

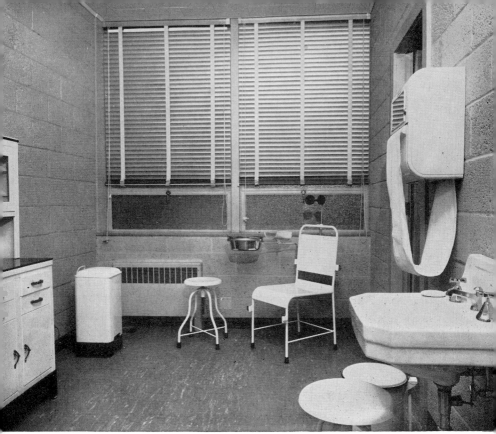

Plate 39. A typical first-aid room for medical treatment.

treatment. Only a physician should put these suggestions for medical treatment into practice. The attending physician, of course, is the one to determine the treatment to be used and the best judge as to what is indicated. However, because many physicians have little occasion to treat conditions due to some chemical exposures, where specific types of treatment have been developed, these are given in case the physician may wish to use them.

So that a physician can be summoned promptly, every laboratory should have posted the names, telephone numbers, and addresses of doctors to be called in an emergency requiring medical care.

To help the attendant physician, a patient suffering from a chemical injury who must be sent to a hospital should be "tagged" with a label giving:

1. Name and address of patient and of employer.

2. Name or type of hazardous material to which he is believed to have been exposed.

3. Specific drugs or treatment that have been administered before transfer.

Burns

Thermal Burns. In the case of minor burns, remove any particles of dirt or adherent material. If area is soiled, cleanse with white soap and distilled water and sponge with 3% hydrogen peroxide, if available. Apply white petrolatum jelly on sterile gauze, cover with thick padding of gauze or cotton and bandage. Refer to a physician for further treatment.

Where there are extensive burns, look out for shock. Notify physician at once. Keep patient as quiet as possible. Avoid chilling. Remove clothing to uncover burn, being careful not to contaminate burned area any more than possible. Do not attempt to cleanse burned area or apply ointments. Cover burned area with sterile gauze or a clean sheet. Remove to hospital as soon as possible. If shock is present, whenever possible get medical attention before sending to the hospital. Send patient in care of an attendant, and notify hospital in advance.

Chemical Burns. A chemical burn is a severe injury involving destruction of tissue following contact with strong acids, alkalies, or oxidizing materials. First aid calls for removal from contact as promptly and completely as possible. When clothing has been contaminated, this means prompt removal of all such clothing, under a shower if possible, not overlooking shoes, garters, etc.

Affected areas of skin should be promptly and freely flushed with water, by shower, hose or whatever other means may be quickly available. This should be done thoroughly. This copious flushing is necessary regardless of the solubility in water of the material involved. The object is to remove mechanically, as quickly as possible, all injurious material.

Do not consider chemical antidotes. Reactions producing further injury may be set up in this way. If later an antidote is to be applied, it should be only as directed by the physician. After flushing to remove all irritant possible, treat as indicated for thermal burns.

Eye Injuries

Foreign Bodies in the Eye. Loose, unattached foreign bodies may often be safely removed with a wet pledget of clean cotton on an applicator. If the particle is attached to the surface of the eye or embedded in it, the case should be referred to a physician, preferably an ophthalmologist. Serious injury may follow "digging" or "picking" at a foreign body as a first aid measure.

Chemical Burns of the Eye. Splashes of irritant chemicals in the eye, or even exposure to vapor or mist of some chemicals, may lead to serious eye injury. Those who may be exposed to such chemicals should always use proper protective goggles or face shields.

First aid should be immediate, and consists of a thorough flushing of the eye with tap water, using eye bath fountain if available, stream of water from a hose, or any other means by which the eye may be freely flushed. Lids should be held apart so that the entire surface of the eye may be flushed. Under most circumstances this flushing should be continued for at least 15 minutes.

The patient should then be referred to a physician, preferably an ophthalmologist with experience in handling chemical burns of the eye. Neutralizing solutions should never be used for first aid, since experience has demonstrated that they often aggravate the injury. Ointments are not recommended for first-aid use.

When referring a case of chemical injury to a physician, if possible, always try to tell him the name of the chemical causing the injury. Some compounds cause very little immediate damage but have a delayed action very evident after a few hours or even days. The extent of damage caused by an acid, for instance, is fairly evident at once, but an alkali may cause markedly progressive damage.

In most laboratories the hazard to the eyes is well recognized in the case of such acids as sulfuric, nitric, hydrochloric, hydrofluoric, etc., but may be overlooked in handling some of the anhydrides, chlorides, etc. Similarly, people are aware of the inherent danger in such alkalies as sodium or potassium hydroxide, lime or ammonia, but may not realize the effects in the case of, for example, many of the amines. This possibility of later damage may be overlooked in instances of exposure to vapors or mists of such materials as hydrogen sulfide, methyl silicate, hydroquinone, etc.

Suggestions as to Medical Treatment. All cases of eye burns should be referred to a physician, preferably an ophthalmologist. A most efficient method of treatment for chemical eye burns, especially from alkaline compounds, is the "denuding" technique. This has been in use for some years and has saved many eyes, but of course should only be carried out by an ophthalmologist experienced in this class of work, and only in the type of eye burn for which it has been found most suitable.[2]

Poisoning

Poisoning is a very general, and loosely used, term commonly connected with swallowing of toxic substances. In this chapter some local irritants have been included, although "poisoning," properly interpreted, should apply only to systemic effects. As encountered in the laboratory, poisoning by swallowing is of rare occurrence. Most important are the hazards from inhalation, and next, from skin absorption.

No attempt has been made to give a long list of poisonous substances with their "antidotes." There are a few compounds for which reasonably specific antidotes are available, the more important of which are mentioned. In general, certain principles of first aid apply. Most important of all is to prevent any hazardous exposure through any route—inhalation, skin contact, or swallowing.

Poisoning by Inhalation. This may occur through exposure to gases, vapors, fumes, mists, or dusts. Some of these are so acutely irritating, or have such marked odors, that these warning

---

[2] This denuding technique is fully described by Ralph S. McLaughlin, M.D., in an article "Chemical Burns of the Human Cornea" in the *American Journal of Ophthalmology* 29:11, November, 1946.

properties make dangerous exposure unlikely, unless the exposed man is physically unable to leave the area of exposure. Such substances include chlorine, bromine, hydrochloric acid, sulfur dioxide, formaldehyde, acrolein, and ammonia.[3]

Other compounds without such prompt irritant action, even though usually having a characteristic odor, may be present in dangerous concentrations before this is realized. Among these are the halogenated hydrocarbons, particularly tetrachloroethane, carbon tetrachloride, methyl bromide, and ethylene chlorhydrin; also such compounds as oxides of nitrogen, hydrofluoric acid, carbon disulfide, and benzene.

Others may have very slight or no odor, even in dangerous concentrations, as in the case of carbon monoxide, methyl chloride, aniline, arsine, and mercury.

Some in higher concentrations—e.g., carbon monoxide, hydrogen sulfide, hydrogen cyanide—cause unconsciousness almost immediately. Others usually have a delayed action, symptoms due to a dangerous exposure not coming on until after a latent period of perhaps some hours. Among these are oxides of nitrogen, phosgene, cadmium fumes, aniline, chlorine, and hydrochloric acid.

Many compounds are dangerous because of the chronic conditions which may result from long exposure to concentrations too low to cause acute symptoms. These include, among others, benzene, carbon tetrachloride and other chlorinated hydrocarbons, mercury, lead, and dusts from a number of solids.

First Aid. Remove patient from exposure as quickly as possible. When victim is in a closely confined space, rescuers may need personal protective equipment such as air-supplied or self-contained breathing apparatus. When exposure has been severe or patient is unconscious, call a physician at once, giving location of patient and whenever possible the identity of the toxic material. Keep patient warm and lying down. If breathing has stopped, start artificial respiration at once. Do not wait for mechanical equipment, but use a manual method immediately. The pre-

---

[3] This group consists of materials where the action is essentially that of an extreme local irritant and the effects cannot properly be classed as "poisoning."

ferred method is the Nielsen arm-lift back-pressure method. This is described as follows:

The victim is placed in the face down or prone position, with the arms folded and the hands placed on top of each other (see Figure 1). The face is then placed on the hands. The operator kneels on either knee, or on both knees, at the victim's head and places his hands under the arms just above the elbows. He lifts them upward at the same time that he rocks backward, drawing the arms toward himself until he meets firm resistance and tension. This is the inspiratory phase. The arms are then replaced on the floor, and the operator moves his hands to the midback (just below the shoulder blades) and rocks forward, keeping his arms stiff, and exerting pressure almost vertically downward to cause active expiration. This expiratory phase may be used to start the method if desired. The complete maneuver is repeated 12 times per minute. Of course, the usual precautions should be taken to see that the tongue, dentures, or other materials are not blocking the victim's airway.

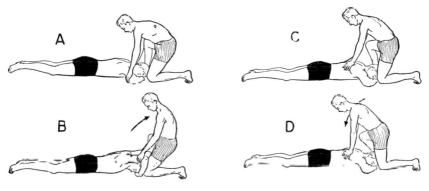

Figure 1.

Whenever artificial respiration is applied, there is usually a definite advantage in the administration of oxygen at the same time. This is especially true in the case of carbon monoxide poisoning. Pure oxygen is usually administered alone, and is preferred, although some use oxygen with 7% carbon dioxide.

Oxygen may be given, preferably through the use of an inhalator or resuscitator. It should be administered only by someone familiar with the procedure, and with the equipment available.

After severe exposure to irritant gases, such as ammonia or chlorine, and especially those known to have a delayed action, such as oxides of nitrogen or phosgene, 100% oxygen should be administered as soon as possible.

Oxygen administration is most effective in irritant gas cases if expiration is made against a positive pressure of 4 cm (about 1¼ inches) of water. This method of oxygen administration should be used only under the supervision of a physician. It may be accomplished readily by use of a rubber tube connected to the outlet valve of a snugly fitting face mask and inserted to a depth of not more than 4 cm below the surface of water in a suitable container. (Special masks are obtainable with adjustable gages which regulate the positive pressure from 1 to 4 cm.) The pressure-resisting exhalation should be adjusted to the patient's tolerance by varying the depth of the end of the tube below the water's surface.

Oxygen inhalation must be continued as long as necessary to maintain the normal color of the skin and mucous membranes. In cases of severe exposure, the patient should breathe 100% oxygen under positive exhalation pressure for half-hour periods every hour for at least 3 hours. If there are no signs of lung congestion at the end of this period, and if breathing is easy and the color is good, oxygen inhalation may be discontinued. Throughout this time, the patient should be kept comfortably warm, but not hot.

The administration of a chemically neutralizing material by inhalation is not recommended as a first-aid measure. Stimulants should be given only as recommended by the attending physician. Adrenalin should not be used in cases involving exposure to chlorinated hydrocarbons, such as carbon tetrachloride.

REMEMBER: Never give anything by mouth to an unconscious patient.

Poisoning by Skin Contact and Absorption through the Skin. Skin contact with various chemicals may result in changes ranging from a defatting action from many solvents not otherwise irritating, to rapid and often deep destruction of tissue in the case of the stronger acids and alkalies. Defatting may only make the skin more sensitive to irritation or secondary infection.

Between this and the direct destruction of tissues, there is a large group of effects described generally as "contact dermatitis." These conditions are so varied, even in different individuals exposed to the same materials, and including the involved question of "sensitization," that their consideration belongs in the field of dermatology rather than in that of laboratory safety.

Skin absorption refers to the systemic effects resulting from absorption through the skin. In the case of some chemicals, the effects due to absorption through the skin are approximately as severe, dose for dose, as from inhalation or swallowing. Such chemicals include allyl alcohol, aniline, ethylene chlorhydrin, ethylene imine among others.

There is a considerable group of chemicals in which toxicity by skin absorption is very definitely a hazard. A few of these are:

Acrylonitrile	Cresols	Tetrachlorethane
Allyl chloride	Cyanides	Toluidine
Antimony trichloride	Nitroaniline	Xylidine
Arsenic trichloride	Phenol	

Also there are economic poisons, such as:

Benzene hexachloride	Parathion
Dimethyl bromide	Tetraethyl pyrophosphate
Nicotine sulfate	

Many chemicals which are definitely hazardous because of toxicity through skin absorption present relatively little or no hazard from local effects. Examples are acrylonitrile, allyl alcohol, aniline, and ethylene chlorhydrin. Others, such as cresol and phenol, have severe local as well as systemic effects.

First Aid. Primary consideration is prompt removal of the chemical from contact with the skin. This is true whether or not the material has local action. All contaminated clothing, including shoes, garters, etc., should be removed at once, preferably under a shower, and the contacted areas freely flushed with water, preferably with plenty of soap, and under a shower or running water. If exposure has been severe, call a physician, telling him the location of the patient and chemical involved.

Copious use of water to remove as far as possible all traces of the chemical is the most available and effective first-aid measure. This applies whether or not the material is water-soluble. Chemical antidotes, such as alkalies for acid contacts and vice versa, or solvents such as alcohol for phenol, should not be used as first-aid measures.

After thorough removal of the chemical, the patient should be kept warm and preferably lying down. Further treatment should be as directed by the physician.

Poisoning by Swallowing

Practically all chemicals handled in a laboratory are "poisonous" if swallowed. It is a question of degree. A broad definition of a poison is "a substance which will injure the body if too much is taken for too long." Should every harmful material be labeled "POISON," the term would soon lose all value as a warning. All chemicals should be treated with due respect according to their properties, but the term "poison" should be reserved only for those which are highly toxic.

First Aid. A physician should be called at once and be told of the location of the patient and if possible the chemical swallowed. If a chemical of known or suspected toxicity has been swallowed, the first step is to remove it from the stomach before it is absorbed. If patient is vomiting, give warm water to drink freely, to aid in vomiting and to dilute any chemical retained in the stomach.

If vomiting is not spontaneous, give lukewarm water freely. It will help to induce vomiting if one or two tablespoonfuls of common salt are dissolved in each glass of water or if a soapy solution is given. One to three teaspoonfuls of powdered mustard may be stirred into each glass of water for the same purpose. Vomiting may also be induced by using a strip of paper to tickle the throat. Vomiting should be encouraged until vomited liquid is clear.

Use of a stomach tube is not recommended as first aid unless such use is by direction of a physician. In the case of corrosive materials it may be dangerous.

After the stomach has been evacuated by free vomiting, the patient should be kept warm, preferably lying down, and watched for shock. In cases of severe poisoning, the patient must also be watched to be sure breathing has not stopped. If breathing has stopped, artificial respiration should be started immediately. Before starting make sure no dentures, tobacco, gum, etc., are in the mouth. Administration of oxygen is often of help in severe cases, whether or not breathing has stopped, but should not be given except by one familiar with its use. Further treatment including use of antidotes, stimulants, etc., should be only as directed by a physician.

REMEMBER: Never give anything by mouth to an unconscious patient.

SPECIFIC ANTIDOTES AND TREATMENT SUGGESTED FOR USE BY PHYSICIANS

Cyanides

In any case of cyanide poisoning call a physician immediately. In all areas in which cyanide compounds are manufactured or handled, a first-aid kit containing the following items should be readily available:

2 boxes (2 dozen) of Amyl Nitrite pearls (ampules)

2 sterile ampules of Sodium Nitrite solution (10 cc of a 3% solution in each)

2 sterile ampules of Sodium Thiosulfate solution (50 cc of a 25% solution in each)

One 10 cc and one 50 cc sterile glass syringe with sterile intravenous needles

One tourniquet

One stomach tube

One dozen gauze pads and 1 small bottle of 70% alcohol

Two 1-pint bottles of 1% Sodium Thiosulfate solution

The kit should be conveniently located and checked at regular intervals by a responsible person.

First Aid. Inhalation and skin contact: The patient should be allowed to breathe the contents of amyl nitrite pearls, one every 5 minutes for twenty minutes. If breathing has ceased, an assistant should administer the amyl nitrite while the patient is receiving artificial respiration. The pearls are to be wrapped lightly in a handkerchief or gauze pad, then broken in the handkerchief or pad and the latter held about one inch from the patient's mouth and nostrils until the strength of the pearl is spent.

WARNING: Those giving first aid should be careful to keep the broken pearls away from their own mouths and noses; otherwise, they may inhale the amyl nitrite, become dizzy, and be rendered incompetent to give proper assistance to the poisoned person.

If cyanide compound has been swallowed, and the patient is conscious, induce vomiting, using as an emetic warm salt water (one tablespoonful of common salt to each cup of water) or one pint of 1% solution of sodium thiosulfate in water. Then continue treatment as above.

REMEMBER: Never give anything by mouth to an unconscious patient.

Suggestions for Medical Treatment. In case of cyanide poisoning, gastric lavage may be performed by a physician. In addition, the physician may administer sodium nitrite and sodium thiosulfate intravenously. The details of this treatment are described in an article by Chen, Rose, and Clowes in the *Journal of the Indiana State Medical Association,* Volume 37 (7) (July, 1944), pages 344-350, "The Modern Treatment of Cyanide Poisoning."

A summary of the treatment is as follows:

1. The physician shows an assistant how to break, one at a time, pearls of amyl nitrite in a handkerchief and hold the latter over the victim's nose for 15 to 30 seconds per minute. At the same time he quickly loads his syringes, one with a 3% solution of sodium nitrite, and the other with a 25% solution of sodium thiosulfate.

2. The physician discontinues the administration of amyl nitrite and injects intravenously 0.3 gm (10 cc of a 3% solution) of sodium nitrite at the rate of 2.5 to 5.0 cc per minute.

3. The physician injects by the same needle and vein, or by a larger needle and a new vein, 12.5 gm (50 cc of a 25% solution) of sodium thiosulfate.

4. The patient should be watched for at least 24 hours, or even 48 hours. If signs of poisoning reappear, the injection of both sodium nitrite and sodium thiosulfate should be repeated, but each in one-half of the above dose. Even if the patient appears perfectly well, the medication may be given for prophylactic purposes 2 hours after the first injections.

WARNING: A patient who has been treated with amyl nitrite, with or without injection of sodium nitrite and sodium thiosulfate, should not be treated with methylene blue.

Hydrofluoric Acid

First Aid. In case of contact with HF, remove contaminated clothing immediately, preferably under a shower. Wash thoroughly all contacted areas with plenty of water. Following this, an ice-cold saturated solution of magnesium sulfate (Epsom salt) or iced 70% alcohol (ethyl or isopropyl) should be applied for at least 30 minutes.

If the burn is in such an area that it is impracticable to immerse the part, then the iced alcohol or the iced magnesium sulfate should be applied with compresses, which should be changed at least every 2 minutes; this treatment should be continued for 30 minutes.

The physician should be on hand to administer treatment before the completion of the magnesium sulfate or alcohol treatment. If, however, he has not arrived by that time, it is then permissible to apply a generous quantity of paste made from powdered magnesium oxide and glycerine U.S.P., and, preferably, freshly prepared. (Oils or greases should not be applied except under instructions from a physician.)

For eyes, flush freely with water for at least 15 minutes. Further treatment should be administered by physician.

Suggestions for Medical Treatment. Treatment after skin contact with liquid or vapor: If the physician sees the patient soon after contact with a diluted (1-20%) solution of hydrofluoric acid, there may be little or no evidence of injury. Evidence of the injury may not appear for several hours.

It is suggested that the affected area be immersed, if possible, in iced 70% alcohol solution. If it is not practicable to immerse the part, then compresses of iced 70% alcohol should be applied. The iced alcohol treatment should be continued for at least 1 hour, because it has a tendency to relieve rapidly the pain which is usually present in this type of burn, and it is quite possible that there is a diffusion of the hydrofluoric acid from the tissues into the alcohol.

As soon as there is evidence of penetration of acid beneath the skin, calcium gluconate solution (1 gm of calcium gluconate in 10 cc of water) should be injected by infiltrating the skin and subcutaneous tissues in the same manner as a local anesthetic is injected subcutaneously. All the skin which has been exposed to the acid should be infiltrated including at least $\frac{1}{4}$-$\frac{1}{2}$ inches around the area. This treatment will usually prevent the development of severe burns.

After treating the affected area with either iced alcohol or iced magnesium sulfate, and after the injection of calcium gluconate solution, magnesium oxide and glycerine paste should be applied. Then the areas should be well padded with gauze and a pressure dressing applied to the area in the same manner as for thermal burns.

In severe burns, blisters filled with a sero-purulent fluid develop and the skin assumes a blanched appearance. Ten per cent calcium gluconate should be immediately injected into and around the affected areas. Blisters should be cut away completely and magnesium oxide and glycerine paste applied to the denuded area for a period of 24-48 hours. At the end of this time, if there is no further evidence of extension of the burned area, magnesium oxide ointment should be applied.

Treatment of Burns around Fingernails. Burns around the fingernails are extremely painful and necessitate special treatment to relieve pain and also to prevent infiltration of the hydrofluoric acid into the deeper structures with the resulting destruction of tissues or even the bone. Eventually such infiltration may necessitate amputation.

The nails should be split from the distal end to the nail bed in order to allow free drainage. A 10% calcium gluconate solution should be injected around and beneath the nail. The affected part should then be soaked in iced alcohol or iced magnesium sulfate for 1½-2 hours.

Contact with the Eyes. Ophthalmologists may be interested in a "denuding" method of treatment for chemical burns of the eye described by Ralph S. McLaughlin, "Chemical Burns of the Human Cornea," *American Journal of Ophthalmology,* **20**:1355, 1946.

Use of a Stomach Tube. If HF is taken internally, induce vomiting. In the use of a stomach tube always consider hazard of perforation. If considered safe on this score, lavage with lime water should be instituted promptly by a physician only. If lime water is not available, milk may be used as a substitute. Soluble calcium inactivates the fluoride ion. In addition to lavage, 10 cc of a 10% solution of calcium gluconate should be injected intravenously. Respiratory depression should be combatted with oxygen and stimulants if necessary; and artificial respiration should be used if needed.

Arsenic Compounds

Give "Universal Antidote" followed by gastric lavage with 240 cc (8 ounces) of 5% sodium bicarbonate solution diluted to 1 liter (1 quart) with warm water, magnesium sulfate 30 gm (1 ounce). Force fluids.

Dimercaprol (BAL) is indicated except in the presence of known liver damage. The following relative to this preparation is from *New and Nonofficial Remedies 1952,* page 427:

"The toxicity of dimercaprol is less in patients suffering from arsenic, gold, or mercury poisoning, but doses of 300 mg. (5 mg. per kilogram of body weight) may produce nausea, vomiting and headache, a burning sensation of the lips, mouth, throat and eyes, generalized muscular aches with burning and tingling of the extremities, and a sense of constriction in the chest. The symptoms usually subside in 30 to 90 minutes.

"DOSAGE: In the treatment of arsenic or gold poisoning, 3 mg. of dimercaprol per kilogram (as a 10% solution in oil) should be administered by intramuscular injection every four hours for the first two days; four injections should be given on the third day; and two injections daily thereafter for ten days, or until complete recovery. In milder cases, the dose may be reduced to 2.5 mg, per kilogram.

"The dosage form listed below is identical to Dimercaprol Injection-U.S.P."

HYNSON, WESTCOTT, & DUNNING, INC.

"Solution BAL in Oil: 4.5 cc ampuls. A solution in peanut oil containing 10% dimercaprol and 20% benzyl benzoate."

Mercury Compounds

Give "Universal Antidote" followed by gastric lavage with 5% sodium formaldehyde sulfoxylate solution, allowing a small amount to remain in the stomach. Inject 100 cc to 200 cc (3⅓-6⅔ ounces) of freshly prepared 5%-10% sodium formaldehyde sulfoxylate solution intravenously. For later treatment give sodium citrate 1-4 gm (15-60 grains) every 4 hours by mouth. Give high colonic irrigation with 1% sodium formaldehyde sulfoxylate solution. Give calcium gluconate 10 cc (2½ drams) of 10% solution intramuscularly or intravenously for muscle spasm.

Treatment by Dimercaprol has been found useful in many cases of mercury poisoning. See Dimercaprol under Arsenic.

Parathion

First Aid. Call a physician at once in all cases of suspected parathion poisoning. If symptoms or signs of poisoning include blurred vision, abdominal cramps, and tightness in the chest, don't wait for a doctor but give two atropine tablets (each 1/100 grains) at once. Remove contaminated clothing and wash the skin clean with plenty of soap and water to remove all traces of parathion. If swallowed, induce vomiting by giving warm salty or soapy water.

REMEMBER: Never give anything by mouth to an unconscious person.

Physician's Note. Warning symptoms include weakness, headache, tightness in the chest, blurred vision, nonreactive pin-point pupils, salivation, sweating, nausea, vomiting, diarrhea, and abdominal cramps.

Treatment. Give atropine, preferably by injection, grains 1/100 two or three tablets at once and parenterally or orally every hour as required up to 30 tablets or until pupils dilate. Never give morphine. Clear chest by postural drainage. Artificial respiration or oxygen administration may be necessary. Observe patient continuously for 48 hours. Repeated exposure to cholinesterase inhibitors may, without warning, cause prolonged susceptibility to very small doses of any cholinesterase inhibitor. Allow no further exposure until time for cholinesterase regeneration has been allowed as determined by blood tests.

"Universal Antidote"

Activated charcoal 2 parts, magnesium oxide 1 part, tannic acid 1 part in a mixture, and given as 15 gm (½ ounce) in a half glass of warm water, may be used to absorb or neutralize poisons. This mixture is useful in poisoning by acids, alkaloids, glycosides, and the heavy metals. After exposure to corrosive substances it should be followed by gastric lavage or an emetic.

CHAPTER XIII

The Packaging and Transportation of Chemicals

The preceding chapters deal with various aspects of the safe handling of chemicals in the laboratory; however, for a more complete orientation of chemical and chemical engineering students, it is advisable that the packaging and transportation of chemicals also be stressed. In doing so, it should be pointed out that the topic in question is of such broad scope that it can be covered here only in a brief manner.

Industry is obliged to comply with numerous requirements in transporting its diverse products, but it is particularly concerned with the safe handling of materials having hazardous characteristics that require them to be regulated for the purpose of transportation and/or storage (for the protection of shippers, carriers, consignees, and consumers) under varying limitations at federal, state, or municipal levels.

This chapter is intended to alert the teaching staff in colleges and universities, and the supervisory personnel in industry, to the fact that hazardous chemicals must be packaged and shipped in accordance with all applicable regulatory requirements. Since the technology of packaging and shipping such chemicals is a highly complicated and specialized field, it cannot be assumed that all members of the teaching profession are sufficiently familiar with the subject, and reliance should therefore be placed on securing outside experts in these techniques to supplement lectures given to chemistry and chemical engineering students who are likely to enter employment in the chemical industry. Such services could be made available through invitation of personnel from chemical manufacturers; state, federal, and municipal regulatory agencies; accredited codemaking bodies such as the National Fire Protection Association; and similar groups. Two or three lectures on this subject should be adequate for the purpose of creating interest on the part of students in this phase of handling chemicals.

The Literature References list a number of Chemical Safety Data Sheets, the contents of which devote considerable text to the shipping and storage of chemical containers. These direct attention to the necessity for observing all pertinent regulations. Interstate Commerce Commission Regulations are most frequently mentioned; however, actual shipping practices demand consideration of all other regulatory requirements which may be applicable, for example, those of the U. S. Coast Guard, Civil Aeronautics Board, Post Office Department, and state or municipal authorities.

The Interstate Commerce Commission derives its power to regulate the packaging and transportation of hazardous chemicals under various acts of the United States Congress.[1] Under Section 835, Title 18, of the United States Code, the Commission is directed to formulate regulations for the safe transportation, within the limits of the jurisdiction of the United States, of explosives and other dangerous articles including flammable liquids, flammable solids, oxidizing materials, corrosive liquids, compressed gases, and poisonous substances (embracing radioactive materials). Such regulations are binding upon all common carriers engaged in interstate or foreign commerce which transport explosives or dangerous articles by land, and upon all shippers making shipments of explosives or dangerous articles via any common carrier engaged in interstate or foreign commerce by land or water. Such regulations must be in accord with the best known practicable means for securing safety in transit, covering the packaging, marking, loading, handling while in transit, and the precautions neces-

[1] U. S. Congress, Act of May 30, 1908 (35 Stat. 555); Act of March 4, 1909 (35 Stat. 1135); Act of March 4, 1921 (41 Stat. 1444); Dangerous Cargoes Act, Oct. 9, 1940 (Title 46, Sec. 465, U. S. Code); and Act of June 25, 1948 (62 Stat. 738, 18 U.S.C.A. 831-835).

sary to determine whether the material when offered is in proper condition to transport.

In the execution of its functions under the statute, the Interstate Commerce Commission is authorized to utilize the services of the Bureau for the Safe Transportation of Explosives and Other Dangerous Articles (now the Bureau of Explosives, Association of American Railroads) and may avail itself of the advice and assistance of any department, commission, or board of the Government.

Interstate Commerce Commission Regulations require the Bureau of Explosives (1) to make inspections and conduct investigations, (2) to confer with manufacturers and shippers with a view to determining what regulations would, within reasonable limits, afford the highest degree of safety in preparing and packaging dangerous articles for transportation, and (3) to make reports of such investigations to the Commission with recommendations, the Commission to give due weight to the expert opinions thus obtained. It is also required that accidents involving the transportation of commodities over which the Commission has jurisdiction must be reported to the Bureau of Explosives.

The regulations place squarely upon the shipper the responsibility to declare the hazardous nature of his shipment and to package, label, and mark the shipment in accordance with the published regulations which are applicable to the shipper. They place on the carrier the responsibility to handle, transport, and stow the dangerous shipments in the manner that is provided in those parts of the published regulations which are applicable to the carriers. Penalties are provided for violations, which are particularly severe if such violations result in injury or death.

The policy of the Bureau of Explosives, since its inception, has been to recognize that manufacturers of dangerous articles have special information regarding the nature and packing of their products, and for that reason they should not only be consulted but invited to participate in the preparation of packaging rules. Although under the law the I.C.C. could disregard this cooperative partnership between shippers and carriers and prescribe rules without consultation, it has never failed (from 1908 until this day) to utilize the recommendations of both in prescribing regulations which have been not only fair and practicable, but as thorough as transportation knowledge would permit. The wisdom of this unique course has proved itself many times during subsequent years, and other regulatory groups have endeavored to promote this same spirit of partnership in their dealings with industry.

In the chemical industry, the preponderance of these cooperative studies are carried on by trade associations which sponsor research and coordinate their individual efforts through technical committees composed of experts drawn from their member firms and frequently the interested regulatory agencies. From the beginning, the Manufacturing Chemists' Association, Inc., has contributed extensively to this work, which has resulted in the present efficient controls of packaging, storage, and transportation of hazardous chemicals, under the helpful rules and regulations prescribed and administered by interested regulatory bodies.

The U. S. Coast Guard, under Federal statute, regulates the transportation of dangerous articles via water, which includes the coasts of the United States, the Great Lakes, and the inland-waterways system. These regulations closely follow the requirements of Interstate Commerce Commission Regulations with certain additional restrictions and modifications as to packaging, stowage, and classes of hazardous materials, in order to assure adequate safety in water transportation.

The Civil Aeronautics Administration is charged with the regulation of dangerous articles handled in aircraft service under requirements published by the Civil Aeronautics Board. These regulations permit certain explosives and various other hazardous articles to be transported by air when legally packed, labeled, and marked. In addition, and within the scope of such regulations, the airlines have issued their own rules on the subject.

Briefly, the Interstate Commerce Commission Regulations serve to furnish the basic requirements with the types and quantities of the acceptable materials being limited by the hazard involved and the class of air carrier.

Passenger-carrying aircraft are restricted to quantities and materials involving the very minimum hazard whereas in the case of cargo aircraft, the regulations are somewhat more liberal and, as far as air service will permit in the interest of safety, closely follow the Commission's requirements applicable to rail express movements.

Postal Laws and Regulations are of important commercial and economic significance in the chemical and other industries due to the substantial volume of chemicals, drugs and medicines, insecticides, germicides, etc., which are shipped to distributors and consumers by mail.

While to a large extent the original urgency for permitting such materials to be handled through the mails was prompted by the necessity for establishing a nationwide service which would adequately provide for agriculture, medicine, and science in rural areas not afforded other modes of fast, readily convenient transportation, it is interesting to note that even with our many up-to-date transportation facilities there are in this country approximately 1,500,000 miles of rural routes serving an estimated 33,000,000 persons. As of June 30, 1952, Illinois, with 1709 routes had the greatest number in any state.

If admitted to the mails by the Postmaster General, hazardous materials are subject to a number of restrictions due in part to factors not encountered in other modes of transportation and for the protection of postal personnel.

The provisions of the law for nonmailable articles and compositions reads:

"All kinds of poison, and all articles and compositions containing poison, and all poisonous animals, insects, reptiles, and all explosives, flammable materials, infernal machines, and mechanical, chemical, or other devices or compositions which may kill or injure another or injure the mails or other property, whether or not sealed as first-class matter, are nonmailable matter and shall not be conveyed in the mails or delivered from any post office or station thereof, nor by any letter carrier.

"The Postmaster General may permit the transmission in the mails, under such rules and regulations as he shall prescribe as to preparation and packing, of any such articles which are not outwardly or of their own force dangerous or injurious to life, health, or property.

"The transmission in the mails of poisonous drugs and medicines may be limited by the Postmaster General to shipments of such articles from the manufacturer thereof or dealer therein to licensed physicians, surgeons, dentists, pharmacists, druggists, cosmetologists, barbers, and veterinarians, under such rules and regulations as he shall prescribe."

By amendment, approved on May 8, 1952, the following was added:

"The transmission in the mails of poisons for scientific use, and which are not outwardly dangerous or of their own force dangerous or injurious to life, health, or property, may be limited by the Postmaster General to shipments of such articles between the manufacturers thereof, dealers therein, bona fide research or experimental scientific laboratories, and such other persons who are employees of the Federal, a State, or local government, whose official duties are comprised, in whole or in part, of the use of such poisons, and who are designated by the head of the agency in which they are employed to receive or send such articles, under such rules and regulations as the Postmaster General shall prescribe."

The importance of the briefly described regulations relative to packaging, labeling, storing, and shipping of hazardous and dangerous chemicals is at once obvious when a chemist or a chemical engineer is confronted for the first time with a new product or an improved old product. As soon as the product assumes interest for possible distribution outside the development and research laboratory, or pilot plant operation, the question is posed as to how to package, label and ship the product; what are its potential hazards in handling, etc. In large industrial establishments, packaging experts are called in to guide the research and development staff. In small manufacturing plants, the superintendent or the manager may have to assume this responsibility. These individuals may rely to some extent on the advice of representatives of local common carriers who are familiar with the rules under which they are permitted to transport a given product. In case of question as to compliance with regulatory provisions, an official expression is obtained from the Bureau of Explosives or the other agencies having jurisdiction. In all this, the uppermost thoughts are: (1) Is the product correctly and safely packaged? (2) Can it be stored safely and for how long a period? (3) Can it be safely transferred from its containers under properly known safeguards to the personnel who handle it? Degrees of toxicity, flammability, or other hazard, if any, must be well known in advance of shipment by the shipper, the carrier, and consumer.

For more complete information relative to the application of principles on packaging, transportation, and storage of specific chemicals, the reader is referred to suggestions outlined in individual Chemical Safety Data Sheets, Manual L-1 "Warning Labels," and other applicable publications. These are set forth under Literature References on pages 217-223 of this volume.

LITERATURE REFERENCES

The subsequent list of references to publications is offered as a general guide for the provision of a basic chemical laboratory library shelf, one that should be particularly useful to students. These publications, manuals, pamphlets, and books deal with various important aspects of safety. The list is not all-inclusive, and librarians, knowing the requirements of a particular student body, may find it advantageous to secure other or additional references.

The references below are not intended to reflect the degree of importance to the sequence in which they are set forth—after listing the MCA publications, alphabetical arrangement has been followed.

MANUFACTURING CHEMISTS' ASSOCIATION, INC.

The MCA issues a series of publications which are considered useful as guides for the safe handling of well-known chemicals. These have received widespread recognition in the United States as well as in foreign countries.

CHEMICAL SAFETY DATA SHEETS

Acetaldehyde	Manual Sheet SD-43
Acetic Acid	Manual Sheet SD-41
Acetic Anhydride	Manual Sheet SD-15
Acetylene	Manual Sheet SD-7
Acrylonitrile	Manual Sheet SD-31
Ammonium Dichromate	Manual Sheet SD-45
Anhydrous Ammonia (Revised)	Manual Sheet SD-8
Aniline	Manual Sheet SD-17
Aqua Ammonia	Manual Sheet SD-13
Benzene	Manual Sheet SD-2
Betanaphthylamine	Manual Sheet SD-32
Bromine	Manual Sheet SD-49
Butadiene	Manual Sheet SD-55
Calcium Carbide	Manual Sheet SD-23
Carbon Disulfide	Manual Sheet SD-12
Carbon Tetrachloride	Manual Sheet SD-3
Caustic Potash	Manual Sheet SD-10

Caustic Soda	Manual Sheet SD-9
Chlorosulfonic Acid	Manual Sheet SD-33
Chromic Acid	Manual Sheet SD-44
Cresol	Manual Sheet SD-48
Dimethyl Sulfate	Manual Sheet SD-19
Ethyl Acetate	Manual Sheet SD-51
Ethyl Chloride	Manual Sheet SD-50
Ethyl Ether	Manual Sheet SD-29
Ethylene Dichloride	Manual Sheet SD-18
Ethylene Oxide	Manual Sheet SD-38
Formaldehyde (Revised)	Manual Sheet SD-1
Hydrochloric Acid	Manual Sheet SD-39
Hydrofluoric Acid	Manual Sheet SD-25
Hydrogen Peroxide	Manual Sheet SD-53
Hydrogen Sulfide	Manual Sheet SD-36
Methanol	Manual Sheet SD-22
Methyl Bromide	Manual Sheet SD-35
Methyl Chloride	Manual Sheet SD-40
Nitric Acid	Manual Sheet SD-5
Nitrobenzene	Manual Sheet SD-21
Ortho-Dichlorobenzene	Manual Sheet SD-54
Paraformaldehyde	Manual Sheet SD-6
Perchloroethylene	Manual Sheet SD-24
Perchloric Acid Solution, Preliminary	Manual Sheet SD-11
Phenol	Manual Sheet SD-4
Phosphoric Anhydride	Manual Sheet SD-28
Phosphorus, Elemental	Manual Sheet SD-16
Phosphorus Oxychloride	Manual Sheet SD-26
Phosphorus Trichloride	Manual Sheet SD-27
Sodium Chlorate (Revised)	Manual Sheet SD-42
Sodium Cyanide	Manual Sheet SD-30
Sodium, Metallic	Manual Sheet SD-47
Sodium and Potassium Dichromates	Manual Sheet SD-46
Styrene Monomer (Revised)	Manual Sheet SD-37
Sulfur Dioxide	Manual Sheet SD-52
Sulfuric Acid (Revised)	Manual Sheet SD-20
Tetrachloroethane	Manual Sheet SD-34
Trichloroethylene	Manual Sheet SD-14
Vinyl Chloride	Manual Sheet SD-56

Other publications of the Association consist of various manuals and pamphlets dealing with specifications for tank cars, drums, tank trucks, and carboys, as well as air and water pollution abatement, labeling, etc. These may directly relate to safety matters in handling chemicals, or give information on the various modes of transportation, storage, and disposal of chemicals in water, streams, and atmosphere.

MANUALS OF STANDARD AND RECOMMENDED PRACTICE

A-10	Fertilizer-Grade Ammonium Nitrate
B-1	Handling and Storage of Paper Shipping Sacks When Filled With Chemicals and Allied Products
C-1	Carboys (ICC-1A) (For Shippers)
C-2	Carboys (ICC-1A) (For Consignees)
C-3	Carboy Bottle (13 gal, cylindrical, straight side ICC Spec. 1A)
C-3A	Carboy Bottle and Closure (6½ gal, ICC Spec. 1D)
C-4	Carboy Stoppers, Porous Earthenware, Spec. & Method of Testing
D-30	Drums, Steel (ICC-5A) (For Shippers)
D-31	Drums (ICC-5A) (For Consignees)
D-32	Faucets, Metal, for discharging contents of steel barrels or drums
D-33	Drums, Steel (ICC-17C and 17E)—When used for shipping flammable liquids flashing between 20° and 80°F.
D-50	Handling and Storage of Fiber Drums
H-10	Hydrofluoric Acid, Anhydrous and Aqueous. Handling and Discharge of Containers
L-1	Warning Labels. Revised, 1953
N-1	Handling of Nitrocellulose Wet with Alcohol (or other Organic Liquid) or Water while in ICC Containers; in Storage or in Process. Revised, 1949
P-1	Air Pollution Abatement Manual—Preface and Outline
P-2	Air Pollution Abatement Manual—Chapter 1. Introduction
P-4	Air Pollution Abatement Manual—Chapter 3. Community Relations
P-5	Air Pollution Abatement Manual—Chapter 4. Legislative Requirements

P-6	Air Pollution Abatement Manual—Chapter 5. Physiological Effects
P-7	Air Pollution Abatement Manual—Chapter 6. Sampling Procedures and Measuring Equipment
P-8	Air Pollution Abatement Manual—Chapter 7. Analytical Methods
P-9	Air Pollution Abatement Manual—Chapter 8. The Meteorology of Air Pollution
P-10	Air Pollution Abatement Manual—Chapter 9. Dust and Mist Collection
P-11	Air Pollution Abatement Manual—Chapter 10. Gas and Vapor Abatement
P-12	Air Pollution Abatement Manual—Chapter 11. Evaluation of Data
P-13	Air Pollution Abatement Manual—Chapter 12. Bibliography
Apndx. 1	Air Pollution Abatement Manual—Bibliography Supplement
Apndx. 2	Air Pollution Abatement Manual—Bibliography Supplement (Appendix Supplements issued every six months)
S-25	Sodium Bisulfate (Niter Cake)—Bulk Shipments in Box Cars
T-1	Table—Aqua Ammonia
T-3	Table—Hydrochloric Acid
T-5	Table—Nitric Acid
T-7	Table—Sulfuric Acid (0—93%)
T-7A	Table—Sulfuric Acid (94—100%)
T-8	Diagram—Oleum Freezing Points
T-9	Table—Zinc Chloride Solution
TC-1	Tank Cars—ICC Spec. 103A, Unloading when filled with sulfuric acid or mixed nitric and sulfuric acids
TC-2	Tank Cars—ICC Spec. 103B, Rubber-Lined—Unloading when filled with Muriatic Acid, Phosphoric Acid, or other authorized liquids
TC-3	Tank Cars—Unloading when filled with liquid Caustic Soda or Caustic Potash (Revised 1946, 1950,, 1952)
TC-4	Tank Cars—Unloading when filled with flammable liquids (Revised, 1952)
TC-6	Tank Cars—Unloading when filled with Phenol

TC-7	Tank Cars—Loading and Unloading Platforms
W-1	Organization and Method for Investigating Wastes in Relation to Water Pollution
W-2	Water Pollution Abatement Manual for Insoluble and Undissolved Substances
W-3	Neutralization of Acidic and Alkaline Plant Effluents

Chemical Facts & Figures, 3rd Edition. A statistical compilation of 420 pages covering the period 1946-1949 inclusive.
(Includes statistics from official sources on chemical production, sales, wholesale prices, foreign trade, employment, etc.)
Chemical Facts & Figures, 2nd Edition. Covers period 1940-1945 inclusive
Technical Data on Plastics, October 1952 Edition
The Chemical Industry Facts Book, First Edition
Literature References

Associations and Other Agencies

American Petroleum Institute, 50 West 50th Street, New York 20, New York. The API issues a series of pamphlets relating to the toxicities of well-known chemicals.
The American Standards Association, Inc., 70 East 45th Street, New York 17, New York. The American Standards Association publishes and distributes many Standards relating to safety.
Compressed Gas Association, Inc., 11 West 42nd Street, New York 36, New York.
Factory Mutual Engineering Division, 184 High Street, Boston 10, Massachusetts. The Loss Prevention Bulletins.
National Fire Protection Association, 60 Batterymarch Street, Boston 10, Massachusetts. The National Fire Codes. NFPA Handbook of Fire Protection.
National Safety Council, 425 North Michigan Avenue, Chicago 11, Illinois. The National Safety Council publishes safety information and safety standards, including the prevention manual, safe practice and health practice pamphlets.
Underwriters' Laboratories, Inc., 207 East Ohio Street, Chicago 11, Illinois. Underwriters' Laboratories, Inc., "Card Data Service" and publication relating to Underwriters' Laboratory listings.

THE UNITED STATES GOVERNMENT

Bureau of Labor Standards, United States Department of Labor, Washington 25, D. C. This Bureau issues a variety of safety pamphlets and statistical information.

United States Bureau of Mines, United States Department of The Interior, Washington 25, D. C. The Bureau of Mines publishes investigation information circulars and bulletins applying to industrial safety and fire protection.

Interstate Commerce Commission, Washington 25, D. C.

1. Code of Federal Regulations, Title 49—Transportation, Parts 71 to 90, Revised 1950.
2. Interstate Commerce Commission Regulations for Transportation of Explosives and Other Dangerous Articles By Land and Water in Rail Freight Service and By Motor Vehicle (Highway) and Water (Including Specifications for Shipping Containers), Effective May 12, 1954. (H. A. Campbell's Freight Tariff No. 9.)

United States Coast Guard

1. United States Coast Guard—Explosives or Other Dangerous Articles on Board Vessels, CG 187, April 9, 1941, Revised July 17, 1950.
2. United States Coast Guard Tank Vessel Regulations, CG123, February 1, 1954.
3. United States Coast Guard Marine Engineering Regulations and Material Specifications, CG115, November 1, 1949.
4. United States Coast Guard Regulations Covering the Transportation, Storage, or Stowage of Explosives or Other Dangerous Articles or Substances, and Combustible Liquids on Board Vessels, Effective June 1, 1941. (H. A. Campbell's Water Carrier Tariff No. 6.)

Civil Aeronautics Board. Civil Air Regulations, Part 49, Transportation of Explosives and Other Dangerous Articles, Effective July 20, 1949.

Post Office Department. Postal Laws and Regulations, Edition of 1948, with effective Supplements.

United States Government Printing Office, Division of Public Documents, Washington 25, D. C. Public Health Service—Industrial Health Publications.

Books

The following books represent some of the important ones recommended for reference libraries:

Industrial Hygiene and Toxicology, Frank A. Patty, Editor, Interscience Publishers, Inc.

Industrial Toxicology, Lawrence T. Fairhall, The Williams and Wilkins Company.

The Merck Index of Chemicals and Drugs, Merck & Co., Inc.

Model Code of Safety Regulations for Industrial Establishments for the Guidance of Government and Industry, International Labour Office, Geneva.

Safety in the Chemical Laboratory, Dr. H. A. J. Pieters, and Dr. J. W. Grayghton, London, Butterworths Scientific Publications.

Safety in the Petroleum Refining and Related Industries, George Armistead, Jr., J. G. Simmonds Co., 1950.

Safety Rules for Use in Chemical Works, Part II, Detailed Instructions, The Association of British Chemical Manufacturers.

Miscellaneous References

The following provide information relating to various aspects of safety.

(1) Industrial Accident Boards
(2) Interstate Commerce Commission (Regulatory Publications)
(3) Insurance Companies
(4) National Council on Compensation Insurance
(5) Various State Departments of Public Health
(6) State Industrial Commissions

Index

Acetic acid, 111-112
Acetylides, 120
Acids:
 chemical hazards, 100-112
 dilute, disposal of, 23
 strong, or mineral, 100
Acrylonitrile, 201
Acute toxicity, 127
Adrenalin, 200
Air, make-up, 15
Air contamination, radiation, 156-157
Airline masks, 189-190
Aisles, layout of, 10-11
Alcohol (ethyl), flammability of, 56
Alkalies:
 chemical hazards, 100, 112-115
 disposal of, 23
 strong and weak, 112
Alkylators, 170
Allyl chloride, 201
Alpha rays:
 defined, 148
 effective distance of travel, 148, 149
American Petroleum Institute, 163, 165
American Red Cross, *Textbook on First Aid*, 193
American Society of Mechanical Engineers, 163, 165
 Unfired Pressure Vessel Code, 167
American Standards Association, 43
Ammonium chromate, 116
Ammonium dichromate, 109-110
Ammonium hydroxide, 115
Anhydrous ammonia, 115
Anhydrous calcium chloride, 140
Aniline, toxicity of, 140-141
Animal experimentation, toxicological information from, 133-134
Antidotes, 193, 197, 203-209
 arsenic compounds, 207-208

Antidotes *(cont.)*:
 cyanides, 203-205
 hydrofluoric acid, 205-207
 mercury compounds, 208
 parathion, 208-209
 universal antidote, 207, 208, 209
Antimony trichloride, 201
Aprons, laboratory, 183, 185
Aqua ammonia, 115
Arsenic compounds, antidotes, 207-208
Artificial respiration, 198-199, 203
Asthma, and exposure to irritants, 130-131
Atmospheric concentration of contaminants, threshold limit values, table, 141-145
Atomic Energy Commission program, 146
Automatic sprinklers, 23, 57

Barium peroxide, 121
Batch autoclaves, 170
Benches:
 aisles between, 10-11
 gases piped to, 17
 sinks, 17
Benzene hexachloride, 201
Benzoic acid, 112
Beta rays:
 defined, 148
 effective distance of travel, 148, 149
 shielding, 151
Block type furnaces, 167-168
Body:
 absorption of radiation, 149-150
 cells and tissues damaged by radiation, 146-147
 protection, 183, 185
Boilers, 171-173
 condensers, 173

225

Boilers (cont.):
  direct fired, 172
  electric heaters, 172
  heat exchangers, 173
  reboilers, 172
  solids heaters, 172
  superheaters, 172
Bombs:
  equipment safeguards, 19
  loading and unloading, 167-168
  pressure vessels, 167-168
Bomb shelters, 168
Boric acid, 112
Bottles:
  glass stoppers in, 37
  labeling, 34
Brine lines:
  construction of, 46
  use of, 45-46, 48
Brine-soaked floors, 45
Bromine, toxicity of, 139
Brushes for cleaning glassware, 37
Bunsen burners, 22
Bureau of Explosives, Association of
    American Railroads, 212-213
Burns, 193
  around fingernails, 206-207
  chemical, 195-196
  nonchemical, 43
  thermal, 195
Butanol, sodium added to, 123

Cabinets, storage, 19
Calcium carbide, 124
Calcium chloride, toxicity of, 140
Calcium hydroxide, 114
Carbon, flammability of, 98
Carbon dioxide, portable extinguish-
    ers of, 57
Carbon monoxide, 198
Carrying containers, glassware, 34
Cast iron drains, 17
Caustic burns, 113, 114
Caustic potash, liquid, 113
Caustic soda, 13
  toxicity of, 135-136
Ceiling lights, 9
Cell damage, radiation, 146-147
Cellulose nitrate, 122
Cement, Portland, 114
Central storerooms, 19, 20
Chemical burns, 195-196
Chemical cartridge respirators, 187

Chemical hazards, 100-124
  acids, 100-112
  alkalies, 100, 112-115
  explosive power, 120-124
  most hazardous chemicals, 100-101
  oxidizing materials, 100, 115-119
Chemical oxygen-producing mask, 189
Chemicals:
  most hazardous, 100-101
  new:
    toxicity of, 133-134
    working with, 130
  packaging and transportation of,
      210-216 (see also Packaging
      and transportation of chemi-
      cals)
  storage of, 13-14
    within laboratory room, 20
  toxic by skin absorption, 201
  toxicological information on, 133-
      134
  waste, disposal of, 23
Chlorates, 116
Chlorine dioxide, 116
Chlorosulfonic acid, 105
Chromates, 116-117
Chrome leather garments, 185
Chromic acids, 108-109
Chromic trioxide, 109
Chronic toxicity, 127
Civil Aeronautics Administration,
    regulations, concerning haz-
    ardous articles, 213
Cleaning:
  cloths for, 48, 51
  of protective equipment, 190
Cleanliness, 22
  of working location, radiation, 153
Clerk, storage, 22
Clothing, safety:
  chrome leather, 185
  contamination of, 128
  flameproof, types of, 183, 185
  protective, radiation, 155, 159
  safety gloves, 92, 136, 152
  safety shoes, 38, 190, 192
  special fire-retardant, 180
Coats, laboratory, 183
Coil reactors, 170-171
Collision hazards, doors, 9
Combustibles:
  oxygen and, 123
  perchloric acid and, 117-119
Compressed air mask, 189

Condensers, 173
Construction of laboratory, 7-10
Consumer products, 135
Contact dermatitis, 201
Containers for chemicals, 13-14
　accident-prevention suggestions, 38, 40
　cylinders, 40-42
　drums, 42
　glassware, carrying, 34
　manifolds, 42
　metal, 34
　　for waste, 23
　plastic, 34
　types of, 38
Contaminated air:
　phenol, 137
　radiation, 156-157
Contamination, 152-153, 156-157
Cork-borer, 44
Cork connections, glass tubing and rods, 30, 32
Corridors, exits into, 10
Cresols, 201
Cutting glass tubing and rods, 30
"Cyanide Poisoning, The Modern Treatment of," Chen, Rose, and Clowes, 204
Cyanides, 201
　antidotes, 203-205
　medical treatment, summary of, 204-205
Cylinders:
　pressure regulators, 41-42
　pressure vessels, 166-167
　suggestions, 40-41

Dead ends, avoiding, 10
Decontamination:
　and hollow type floors, 9
　radiation, 153-156 (see also under Radiation)
Design:
　equipment, 10-24
　laboratory, 7-10
Desks, separated from benches, 11
Devolatilizers, 170
Diketene, polymerization of, 122
Dimercaprol, toxicity and doses of, 207-208
Dimethyl bromide, 201
Disks, rupture, in pressure vessels, 163, 165
Disposal traps in sinks, 17

Doors:
　into corridors, 10
　exit, 7-8
　in fire walls, 9, 24
　glazed, 14
　of hoods, 14
　number of, 8-9
　outswinging, 8, 9
　vertical, 14
Drains, duriron or cast iron, 17
Drawers, storage, 19
Drugs, flammable, 98
Drums, 42
Dry chemical extinguishers, 57
Duriron drains, 17
Dusts, 197
　flammable, 98-99
　mineral, atmospheric concentration of, table, 144
　radioactive, safeguards, 153
　sodium hydroxide, 135
　toxic, atmospheric concentration of, table, 144
Dynamite, 122

Economic poisons, 201
Education of personnel, radiation, 159-160
Electrical layouts, 17, 19
Electric heaters, 172
Electricity, static, 42
　generated by clothing, 185
Elevators, 51
Emetics, 202-203, 204
Equipment, 10-24
　aisles between, 10-11
　layout of, 10-13
　pressure vessels (see Pressure vessels)
　protective:
　　cleaning and servicing, 190
　　eye and face, 182-183
　　familiarity with, 180
　　location of, 180-182
　　radiation, 155
　　respiratory, 185-190
　safeguards, 19
　working surfaces and, radiation, 154
Ether, flammability of, 56
Ether peroxides, 121
Exhaust fans, hoods, 14, 15
Exhaust hoods (see Hoods)
Exhaust systems, 16

Exit doors, 7-8, 10
Explosions of dust, preventing, 98-99
Explosive limits, flammable materials, 55
Explosive power, chemical hazards, 120-124
Explosive range, flammable materials, 55
Explosives, Bureau of, Association of American Railroads, 212-213
Exposure to chemicals, types of, 128-129
Extension cords, electric, 19
Extinguishing agents, 56-57
Eyes:
  aniline, 140
  bromine, 139
  calcium chloride, 140
  chemical burns, 196-197
  contact with, 128
  foreign bodies in, 196
  hydrofluoric acid, 102, 205, 207
  injuries to, 193
  medical treatment, 197
  nitric acid, 106
  phenol, 136
  safety glasses, 135, 136, 180, 182-183
  shields for, 136
  sodium hydroxide, 135
  sulfuric acid, 104
Eye-wash equipment, 17
Eye-wash station, location of, 17

Face protection, 182-183
  safety glasses, 135, 136, 180, 182-183
  shields, 136
Falls and slips, 48, 51
Fans, exhaust, hoods, 14, 15
Fertilizers, flammability of, 98
Film badges and rings, radiation, 157, 158, 159
Filters, classified, 185, 187
Fingernails:
  burns around, 206-207
  hydrofluoric acid and, 102
Finger rings, 51
Fire extinguishers, location of, 23-24
Fire-hazard properties of flammable materials, 53-57
Fire protection, 23-24
  fire alarm system, 24
Fire walls, 24
  doors in, 9

First Aid, Textbook on, American Red Cross, 193
First aid and medical treatment, 193-209
  antidotes, 203-209 (see also Antidotes)
  artificial respiration, 198-199
  burns, 195-196
  eye injuries, 196-197
  oxygen, administration of, 199-200
  poisoning, 197-203
    by inhalation, 197-200
    by skin contact and absorption, 200-202
    by swallowing, 202-203
  tag for patient to be sent to hospital, 194-195
  unconscious patient, 200, 203, 204, 208
  vomiting, inducing, 202-203, 204, 207, 208
First-aid kit, cyanide poisoning, 203
Flame, propagation of, meaning of, 54 n.
Flameproof clothing, types of, 183, 185
Flammable materials, handling, 52-99
  dusts, 98-99
  explosive limits of, 55
  explosive range of, 55
  extinguishing agents, 56-57
  fire-hazard properties of, 53-57
  flash point of, 54
  ignition temperature of, 54-55
  references, 95-98
  Table of Common Hazardous Chemicals, 57-95
  Underwriters' Laboratories classification, 56
Flash point of liquid, 54
Floors:
  brine-soaked, 45
  electrical hazards, 44-45
  hollow-type construction, 9
  around safety showers, 17
Foam type extinguishers, 57
Food products and by-products, flammable, 98
Foot protection, 190, 192
Formic acid, 111
Fumes, 197
  toxic, atmospheric concentration of, table, 144
Furnaces, block type, 167-168

Furniture:
  aisles between, 10-11
  layout, 10-13

Gamma rays:
  defined, 148
  effective distance of travel, 149
  toxicity of, 145
Gases, 197
  atmospheric concentration of, table, 142-143
  fire hazard properties of, 53-57
    table, 57-95
  ignition temperature of, 54-55
  piped to benches, location of, 17
  storage of, 21-22
Gas fires, extinguishing, 57
Gas masks, 187-190
  canister type, 187-188
Gasoline, flammability of, 56
Glass:
  bombs, 167
  broken, disposal of, 13, 14, 23, 37
  safety, 11
    laminated, 14
    as shield, 11
Glasses, safety, 135, 136, 180, 182-183
Glassware:
  bottles, outage in, 33
  cleaning, 36-37
  cleaning solutions, 109
  handling, 25-37
  heating, 33
  holding, 34
  inspecting, 25
  pressure relief for, 33
  pressurizing, 33
  receiving, 25
  and rubber or cork connections, 30, 32
  selecting, 28
  setting up apparatus, 28, 30
  on shelves, 34, 36
  stoppers in bottles, frozen, 37
  storing, 19, 25, 27
  tubing and rods:
    cutting, 30
    positioning, 30
    removing, 30, 32
    storing, 27
Gloves, safety, 92, 136
  lead impregnated, X-ray technicians', 152
Gunpowder, 122

Hammers, 44
Hand protection, 92, 136, 152, 192
Hand tools, 44
Hazard differentiated from toxicity, 131-133
Heaters:
  electric, 172
  solids, 172
  superheaters, 172
Heat exchangers, 173
Heating of glassware, 33
Hoods, 13-16
  air flow of, 15
  construction of, 14
  controls, location of, 16
  exhaust fan, 14, 15
  location of, 12
  for perchloric acid, 119
Hose:
  care of, 22
  fog nozzle vs. streams, 56
  location of, 24
Hougen and Watson, *Chemical Process Principles*, 166, 167
Housekeeping, 22-23
Hydrochloric acid, 110
Hydrofluoric acid, 101-103
  antidotes, 205-207
  injury prevention, 103
Hydrogen peroxide, 121
Hypersensitivity, 131

Ignitible mixture, meaning of, 54
Ignition temperature of mixture, 54
  55
Industrial Hygiene Standards, lists of, 134
Inhalation, poisoning by, 197-200
  aniline, 141
  bromine, 139
  calcium chloride, 140
  contaminated air, 128
  hydrofluoric acid, 102
  nitric acid, 106-108, 138
  phenol, 137
  sodium hydroxide, 135
  sulfuric acid, 104
Injection of chemicals, 129
Injuries, local and systemic, 126-127
Insecticides, flammable, 98
Inspection:
  of glassware, 25
  of pilot-scale operations, 163

Interstate Commerce Commission Regulations, packaging and transportation of chemicals, 211-212

Kerosene, flammability of, 56
Kettles, 171
Key men, rules for, 1

Labeling:
  bottles, 34
  cylinders, pressure vessels, 166
  patients to be sent to hospitals, 194-195
  services, 16
Laboratories, private or small, occupancy, 11
Laboratory safety, general rules, 1-6
  common standards, 2-3
  important phases of program, 4, 6
  key men, 1
  representative safety program, 3-4
Ladders, 43
Layout:
  electrical, 17, 19
  furniture and equipment, 10-13
Lighting, ceiling lights, 9
Lime, 114
Liquid air, 123
Liquid caustic potash, 113
Liquid oxygen, 123
Liquids, flammable:
  classification of flammability, 56
  fire hazard properties of, 53-57
    table, 57-95
  flash point of, 54
Literature references, 217-223
  associations and agencies, 221
  books, 222-223
  miscellaneous references, 223
  U. S. Government publications, 221-222
Local injuries, 126-127
Lye, 113
  toxicity of, 135-136

McLaughlin, Ralph S., 197, 207
Mails, hazardous materials in, 214-215
Maleic acid, 112
Manhole requirements, pressure vessels, 179
Manifolds, 42

Manufacturing Chemists' Association, 193
  packaging and transportation of chemicals, 213
  publications of, 217-221
Masks, 180, 182
  airline, 185, 189-190
  compressed air, 189
  gas, 187-190 (see also Gas masks)
  self-contained types, 188-189
Maximum allowable concentrations (MAC), 126, 134
Medical examinations, radiation, 155
Medical treatment (see First aid and medical treatment)
Mercuric oxide, 120
Mercury, spilled, care of, 22-23
Mercury compounds, antidotes, 208
Metal:
  containers, 34
  fumes respirators, 185, 187
  powders, flammable, 98
  sodium, 123-124
Milliroentgen, defined, 147 n.
Mists, 197
  toxic, atmospheric concentration of, table, 144
Monel wire, 46
Monitoring, radiation (see under Radiation)
Mortar, 114
Multiple-story buildings:
  exits, 7
  ventilation, 16

Nails, 44
National Board of Fire Underwriters, 7
National Bureau of Standards, handbooks on radiation, 151
National Electrical Code, 9
National Fire Protection Association, 53, 211
  Fire Codes, 21, 56, 99
  organization of, 53
  standards for blower and exhaust systems, 16
  Table of Common Hazardous Chemicals, 57-95
National Safety Council, material on dusts, 98
Neatness, 22
Neutrons, 148 n.

New and Nonofficial Remedies 1952,
    quoted, 207-208
New chemicals:
    toxicity of, 133-134
    working with, 130
Nicotine sulfate, 201
Nielsen, artificial respiration, 198-199
Nitric acid, 106
    gaseous oxides of, 107
Nitroaniline, 201
Nitrogen-containing compounds, 120
Nitrogen iodide monoamine, 120
Nitroglycerine, 122
Noncombustible construction, 7

Occupancy, in private and small laboratories, 11
Ointments, 196
Oral intake, 129, 202-203
    hydrofluoric acid, 103
    nitric acid, 108
    sulfuric acid, 104
Organic nitrogen compounds, 122
Outswinging doors, 8, 9
Overalls, laboratory, 183
Overstocking, avoiding, 19
Oxidizing materials, chemical hazards, 100, 115-119
Oxygen:
    administration of, 199-200, 203
    and combustibles, 123
    liquid, 123

Packaging and transportation of chemicals, 210-216
    Bureau of Explosives, Association of American Railroads, 212
    Civil Aeronautics Board, 213
    Interstate Commerce Commission Regulations, 211-214
    Manufacturing Chemists' Association, 213
    penalties for violations, 212
    Postal Laws and Regulations, 214-215
    transportation:
        by land, 211
        on passenger-carrying aircraft, 213-214
        by water, 213
    U. S. Coast Guard, 213
Pain, sense of, 129-130
"Panic" hardware, doors equipped with, 9

Paper, flammability of, 98
Paracetic acid, 122
Paraffin oil, flammability of, 56
Parathion, 201
    antidotes, 208-209
Passageways, care of, 22
Peg boards, sinks, 17
Penetrating radiation, 151-152
Perchloric acid, 117-119
Peroxides, 121
Personnel, radiation (*see under* Radiation)
Phenol, 201
    toxicity of, 136-137
Phosphoric acid, 111
Photographic darkrooms, 8
Physician, 193, 194
Picric acid, 122
Pilot-scale operations, inspection and testing, 163
Pipe, brine, 46
Piping, floor openings around, 24
Plastic, containers, 34
Plugs, fusible, for cylinders, 166
Plumbing, 16-17
Poison, defined, 202
Poisoning, 193
    by inhalation, 197-200
    by skin contact and absorption, 200-202
    by swallowing, 202-203
Poisons, economic, 201
Polymerization, 122-123
    cylinders, 166
Polymerizers, 168, 170
Portland cement, 114
Postal laws and regulations, packaging and transportation of chemicals, 214-215
Potassium, 109-110
Potassium chromate, 116
Potassium dichromate, 117
Potassium hydroxide, 113-114
Potentiation, meaning of, 131
Pressure regulators on cylinders, 41-42
Pressure vessels, 162-179
    boilers, 171-173
    bombs, 167-168
    cylinders, 166-167
    file for each vessel, 162-163
    manhole requirements, 179
    reactors, 168, 170-171
    refrigeration equipment, 173
    relief valves, 163, 165

Pressure vessels (*cont.*):
  rupture disks, 163, 165
  safety devices, 163, 165-166
  selection, inspection, and testing
    systems, 162-163
  service log history, 163
  storage tanks, 173, 177-179
  supervisor, responsibility of, 166
Pressurizing glassware, 33
Propagation of flame, meaning of,
    54 *n.*
Propanol, sodium added to, 123
Protective equipment (*see* Equip-
    ment: protective)
Pulmonary edema, 101, 107, 108, 111

Radiation, 146-161
  alpha, beta, and gamma rays (*see
    under separate headings*)
  biological effects of, 149
  bodily absorption of, 149-150
    safeguards, 153
  contamination, 152-153
    areas, designation of, 154-155
    defined, 152
    levels, measures of, 156
    natural decay of, 154
  control measures, 150-152
    basis of, 150-151
    distance between source and
      worker, 151
    general, 150-151
    length of work time, 152
    penetrating radiation, 151-152
    shielding, 150, 151
  decontamination, 153-156
    air-borne material, 156
    areas, designation of, 154-155
    defined, 153-154
    means of, 154
    medical examinations, 155
    personnel, restriction of, 155
    protective clothing and equip-
      ment, 155
    waste disposal, 155-156
  detection instruments, 156-158
    air contamination, 156-157
    environment survey type, 156
    personal badges, 157
    personnel monitoring devices,
      157-158
  internal, elimination of, 152
  maximum possible dose, 147-148

Radiation (*cont.*):
  monitoring:
    environmental, 159
    film badges, 157, 158, 159
    frequency of, 159
    personnel, 157, 158
  personnel:
    monitoring devices, 157, 158
    responsibility of, 159, 161
    restriction of, 155
    protective surface coverings, use of,
      154
    radioactive dusts, safeguards, 153
    rays, defined, 148
    records, 158-159
    supervision, responsibility of, 161
    surface contamination, removal of,
      153-154
    tissue and cell damages, 146-147
    tolerance, 147
    toxicity of, 145
    working surfaces and equipment,
      154
  X-rays, 145, 146
Radioactive dusts, safeguards, 153
Reactors:
  alkylators, 170
  batch autoclaves, 170
  coil, 170-171
  devolatilizers, 170
  kettles, 171
  polymerizers, 168, 170
  pressure vessels, 168, 170-171
  vaporizers, 171
Reagents:
  location of, 12-13
  shelves for, 34, 36
  stock, storage of, 20
Reboilers, 172
Records:
  glassware, 25
  pressure vessels, 162-163
  radiation, 158-159
Refrigerants, 48
Refrigeration equipment, pressure
    vessels, 173
Refrigerator, 21
Relief valves, pressure vessels, 163,
    165
Respirators, 185
  classified, 185, 187
Respiratory protection, 185-190
  gas masks, 187-190
  respirators, 185, 187

Rhodium-*106*, 150-151
Rings:
  film badges and, 157, 158, 159
  finger, 51
Rods:
  control, shield holes in, 151
  glass, 27, 30
Roentgen rays, 146
  defined, 147 *n.*
  toxicity of, 145
Rubber:
  aprons, 185
  connections, glass tubing and rods,
    30, 32
  gloves, 192
  hard, flammable, 98
  safety shoes, 190
  sterilization of, 190
Rupture disks, pressure vessels, 163,
  165
Ruthenium-*106*, 150

Safe load, cylinders, 166
Safety, laboratory, general rules, 1-6
Safety factor, 134
Safety glass, 11, 14
Safety glasses, 135, 136, 180, 182-183
Safety organization, chart, 5
Safety shields, 11, 136
Safety showers, 12, 17, 38
Sage and Lacey, *Industrial and Engi-
  neering Chemistry*, 166, 167
Sensitivity to chemicals, 130-131
Sensitization, 201
Servicing protective equipment, 190
Shelters, bomb, 160
Shelves:
  for reagents, glassware on, 34, 36
  storage, 19, 20, 22
Shielding, radiation, 150, 151
Shields, safety, 11, 136
Shippers of chemicals, responsibility
  of, 212
Shoes, safety, 38, 190, 192
  contamination of, 128
Showers, safety, 17, 38
  location of, 12
Silver fulminate, 120
Sinks, 17
Skin contact and absorption, poison-
  ing by, 200-202
  aniline, 140-141
  calcium chloride, 140
  contact with, 128

Skin contact and absorption (*cont.*):
  hydrofluoric acid, 102
  nitric acid, 106
  phenol, 136-137
  sodium hydroxide, 135
  sulfuric acid, 104
Slips and falls, 48, 51
Smell, sense of, 129
Smocks, laboratory, 183
Sodium, disposal of, 123
Sodium chromate, 116
Sodium dichromate, 109-110, 117
Sodium hydroxide, 113
  toxicity of, 135-136
Solids, volatile:
  fire hazard properties of, 53-57
  flash point of, 54
  ignition temperature of, 54-55
Solids heaters, 172
Solvents, flammable, storage of, 20-21
Sodium metal, 123-124
Sodium peroxide, 121
Spices, flammability of, 98
Sprinkler systems, automatic, 23
Stairways, construction of, 7
Standpipe systems, location of, 24
Static electricity, 42
  generated by clothing, 185
Sterilization methods, 190
Stomach tube, use of, 207
Stoppers, rubber, cork, or glass, 30,
  32
Storage:
  central storerooms, 19, 20
  of chemicals, 13-14
  cylinders, 10
  drums, 42
  of glassware, 25, 27
  space for, 19-22
  of waste, 13
Storage clerk, 22
Storage tanks, 173, 177-179
Succinic acid, 112
Sulfur, flammable, 98
Sulfuric acid, 103-105
  injury prevention, 104-105
Superheaters, 172
Swallowing:
  of chemicals, 129
  poisoning by, 202-203
Synergism, meaning of, 131
Synthetic materials, protective cloth-
  ing, 183, 185
Systemic injuries, 126-127

Table of Common Hazardous Chemicals, 57-95
Tanks, storage, atmospheric pressure type, 173, 177-179
Tanning materials, flammability of, 98
Tetrachlorethane, 201
Tetraethyl pyrophosphate, 201
Textbook on First Aid, American Red Cross, 193
Thermal burns, 195
Threshold limit values for 1953, atmospheric concentration of contaminants, table, 141-145
Tissue damage, radiation, 146-147
Tobacco, flammability of, 98
Tolerance:
 of irritants, 130-131
 radiation, 147
Toluidine, 201
Tools, hand, 44
Toxicity, 125-145
 acute, 127
 chronic, 127
 exposure, types of, 128-129
 hazard differentiated from, 131-133
 hypersensitivity, 131
 illustrative materials, 134-141
   aniline, 140-141
   bromine, 139
   calcium chloride, 140
   phenol, 136-137
   sodium hydroxide, 135-136
 maximum allowable concentrations (MAC), 126
 pairs of drugs, 131
 qualitative effects, 126-127
 quantitative effects, 125-126
 ranges of, 126
 susceptibility to, 130-131
 threshold limit values for 1953, table, 141-145
 tolerance and sensitivity, 130-131
 warning senses, 129-130
Toxicological information, use of, 133-134
Traps, fixture, 17
Trash, storage and removal of, 13
Trinitrotoluene, 122
Tubing, glass, 27, 30, 32
Transportation and packaging of chemicals, 210-216 (*see also* Packaging and transportation of chemicals)

"U" aisle, 10
Unconscious patient, 200, 203, 204, 208
Universal antidote, 207, 208, 209
U. S. Coast Guard, regulation of transportation of chemicals, 213
U. S. Government publications, 221, 222

Vacuum, containers under, 34
Valves:
 in cylinders, 166
 pressure-vacuum relief, 163, 165, 177, 179
Vapor density, flammable materials, 55-56
Vaporizers, 171
Vaporizing liquid extinguishers, 57
Vapors, 197
 atmospheric concentration of, table, 142-143
Vestibules, doors recessed in, 9
Ventilation:
 ducts, in fire-resistant shafts, 9, 16
 hoods, 13-15
Vinyl compounds, polymerization of, 123
Volatile solids, fire hazard properties of, 53-57
 table, 57-95
Vomiting, inducing, 202-203, 204, 207, 208

Warning Labels, MCA Manual L-1, 34
Warning senses, 129-130
Washing glassware, 36
Waste:
 disposal of, 22-23
   radioactive materials, 155-156
 storage and removal of, 13
Waste sewer, industrial, 17
Water:
 extinguishing agent, 56-57
 outlets, care of, 22
Windows, 9
 explosion-venting, 10
Wiring, electrical, 45
Wood dusts, flammability of, 98

X-rays, 147 *n,* 148, 149
 discovery of, 146
Xylidine, 201